# Homework Book

C000192544

## MyMaths
### for Key Stage 3

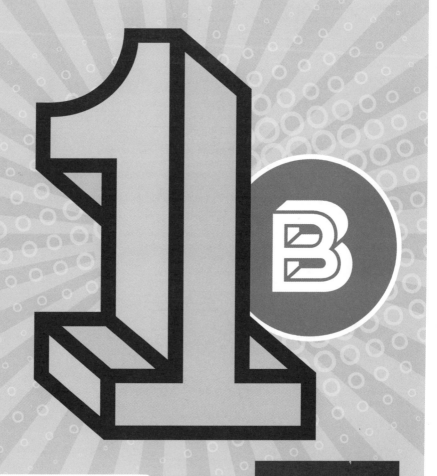

1B

powered by MyMaths.co.uk

OXFORD
UNIVERSITY PRESS

# OXFORD
UNIVERSITY PRESS

Great Clarendon Street, Oxford OX2 6DP

Oxford University Press is a department of the University of Oxford.
It furthers the University's objective of excellence in research, scholarship,
and education by publishing worldwide in

Oxford   New York

Auckland   Cape Town   Dar es Salaam   Hong Kong   Karachi
Kuala Lumpur   Madrid   Melbourne   Mexico City   Nairobi
New Delhi   Shanghai   Taipei   Toronto

With offices in

Argentina   Austria   Brazil   Chile   Czech Republic   France   Greece
Guatemala   Hungary   Italy   Japan   Poland   Portugal   Singapore
South Korea   Switzerland   Thailand   Turkey   Ukraine   Vietnam

© Oxford University Press

British Library Cataloguing in Publication Data

Data available

ISBN 978-0-19-830445-6
10 9 8 7 6 5 4 3

Printed in Great Britain

MIX
Paper from
responsible sources
FSC   FSC® C007785

# Contents

# 1a   Place value and decimals

**Example**

Write the value of each of the digits in the number 375.291

---

3 thousands, 7 hundreds, 5 units, 2 tenths, 9 hundredths and
1 thousandth.

**1** Write each of these numbers in words.
  **a** 729　　**b** 3265　　**c** 19362　　**d** 2536417
  **e** 37.4　　**f** 45.63　　**g** 86.05　　**h** 417.92

**2** Write each of these numbers in figures.
  **a** Four hundred and fifty-two
  **b** Five thousand and fifty
  **c** Twenty-three thousand and three
  **d** Twenty-five and three tenths
  **e** Thirty-six, three tenths and seven thousandths
  **f** One hundred and fifty-three and eight hundredths

**3** Give the value of the digit 4 in each of these numbers.
  **a** 347　　**b** 6435　　**c** 54.32
  **d** 96.74　　**e** 3.429　　**f** 9.154

**4** Write these numbers in order, starting with the smallest.
  **a** 4.2, 4.06, 4.15, 4, 4.8
  **b** 2.05, 2.5, 2.55, 2.25, 2.2
  **c** 0.1, 0.13, 0.14, 0.137, 0.3

**5** Shani's dog has a litter of six puppies. Their weights are:
Toby 1.44 kg, Prince 1.55 kg, Jessie 1.50 kg, Dumpy 1.45 kg,
Sally 1.40 kg and Rover 1.54 kg.

Write their names in order of weight, starting with the heaviest.

**Example**

**a** Calculate $7.32 \times 100$

**b** Find the missing number in $84.2 \div ? = 0.0842$

---

**a** $7.32 \times 100 = 732$    The digits move two places to the left.

**b** $84.2 \div 1000 = 0.0842$    The digits have moved three places to the right, so 84.2 has been divided by 1000.

**1** Copy and complete these statements.

  **a** $\square \times 10 = 2.5$    **b** $87 \div 10 = \square$

    $0.25 \times \square = 25$      $87 \div \square = 0.87$

    $0.25 \times 1000 = \square$      $\square \div 1000 = 0.087$

**2** Calculate each of these.

  **a** $14 \times 10$    **b** $5 \times 100$

  **c** $3 \times 1000$    **d** $5.2 \times 10$

  **e** $2.8 \times 1000$    **f** $4.36 \times 10$

  **g** $34.5 \times 100$    **h** $0.63 \times 10$

**3** Calculate each of these.

  **a** $280 \div 10$    **b** $5000 \div 100$

  **c** $23\,000 \div 1000$    **d** $165 \div 10$

  **e** $410 \div 100$    **f** $52.7 \div 10$

  **g** $1.9 \div 10$    **h** $846 \div 1000$

**4** By writing each multiplier as two of its factors, calculate these.

  **a** $5 \times 20 = 5 \times 2 \times \square =$

  **b** $3 \times 900 = 3 \times \square \times 100 =$

  **c** $7 \times 40 = 7 \times \square \times \square =$

  **d** $11 \times 500 =$

  **e** $12 \times 70 =$

  **f** $15 \times 400 =$

# 1c Negative numbers

Josiah has £100 in his bank account.
What will his balance be if he withdraws £250?

£100 − £250 = −£150, so he will be £150 overdrawn.

1 Put these numbers in order from lowest to highest.
   a  −3      8       4       0        −15
   b  −24     6       −16     −17      1
   c  4       −3      2       3        −9

2 Work out these.
   a  5 − 10        b  9 − 12        c  15 + −9        d  5 + −9
   e  10 + −16      f  −5 + −11      g  −4 − −9        h  −12 − −16
   i  −12 − −4      j  15 − −6       k  19 − −5        l  −20 − −8

3 Candace's bank balance is −£250. Find what her balance would
   be if she paid in
   a  £100         b  £200          c  £400          d  £500.

4 Kanika recorded the midday temperature outside her
   house on each day of one week.

| Monday | Tuesday | Wednesday | Thursday | Friday | Saturday | Sunday |
|---|---|---|---|---|---|---|
| 9 °C | 4 °C | −2 °C | −5 °C | −3 °C | 3 °C | 6 °C |

   a  Find the fall in temperature from
      i   Monday to Tuesday
      ii  Tuesday to Wednesday.
   b  Find the rise in temperature from
      i   Thursday to Friday
      ii  Friday to Saturday.

> Use a mental method to calculate **a** $13.2 + 6.9$ **b** $165 - 94$
>
> - - - - - - - - - - - - - - - - - - - - - - - - - - - - - - - - - - - - - - -
>
> **a** Split 6.9 into 6 and 0.9    $13.2 + 6.9$    $= 13.2 + 6 + 0.9$
>                                                  $= 19.2 + 0.9 = 20.1$
>
> **b** Split 94 into 90 and 4    $165 - 94$    $= 165 - 90 - 4$
>                                                  $= 75 - 4 = 71$

**1** Copy and complete the crosswork frame.

| Across | Down |
|--------|------|
| **1.** $109 + 16$ | **1.** $100 - 81$ |
| **3.** $102 + 34$ | **2.** $110 - 86$ |
| **5.** $49 + 45$ | **3.** $201 - 99$ |
| **6.** $80 + 25$ | **4.** $168 - 133$ |
| **7.** $73 + 59$ | **6.** $190 - 55$ |
| **10.** $39 + 26$ | **7.** $210 - 42$ |
| **11.** $54 + 45$ | **8.** $199 - 150$ |
| **12.** $103 + 15$ | **9.** $111 - 40$ |
| **14.** $13 + 11$ | **11.** $121 - 27$ |
| **15.** $47 + 38$ | **13.** $255 - 132$ |
| **17.** $110 + 125$ | **14.** $290 - 38$ |
| **18.** $141 + 115$ | **16.** $131 - 105$ |

**2** Use partitioning to work out these questions mentally.

For example, $12 + 5.7 = 12 + 5 + 0.7 = 17.7$

  **a** $19 + 6.4$           **b** $8.6 + 3.2$

  **c** $16 - 3.9$           **d** $4.8 - 3.2$

  **e** $4.5 + 3.6$          **f** $6.5 - 2.7$

  **g** $12.7 + 4.8$        **h** $22.3 - 8.5$

**3** Use compensation to work out these questions mentally.

For example, $2.4 + 3.9 = 2.4 + 4 - 0.1 = 6.3$

  **a** $6.5 + 2.9$           **b** $12.5 + 4.9$

  **c** $7.3 - 3.9$           **d** $23.6 - 12.9$

MyMaths.co.uk

🔍 1345, 1380   SEARCH

## and subtraction

**Example**

Calculate    **a** 3.4 + 4.68    **b** 35.1 − 21.3

**a** Estimate: 3 + 5 = 8    Written method: 3.4
$$\begin{array}{r} 3.4 \\ +4.68 \\ \hline 8.08 \end{array}$$

**b** Estimate: 35 − 21 = 14    Written method:
$$\begin{array}{r} 35.1 \\ -21.3 \\ \hline 13.8 \end{array}$$

**1** Calculate these using a written method.
   **a** 425 + 213   **b** 841 + 226   **c** 327 + 143   **d** 933 + 419
   **e** 653 + 281   **f** 752 + 297   **g** 458 + 364   **h** 849 + 387

**2** Calculate these using a written method.
   **a** 649 − 217   **b** 593 − 452   **c** 342 − 128   **d** 653 − 417
   **e** 816 − 334   **f** 509 − 235   **g** 642 − 353   **h** 825 − 257

**3** Calculate these using a written method.
   **a** 84.2 + 31.7   **b** 29.5 − 15.3   **c** 24.9 − 14.3   **d** 75.8 − 47.3
   **e** 46.2 + 5.19   **f** 86.4 + 7.92   **g** 9.38 − 4.5   **h** 85.2 − 37.03

**4** Use a written method to solve each of these problems.
   **a** A removal man pushes a piano on a trolley into a lift cage.
   The man weighs 90 kg, the trolley 65 kg and the piano 244 kg.
   What is the total weight?
   **b** A notice in the lift cage says 'Maximum weight 400 kg'. Is the weight
   within this limit? If so, by how much?
   **c** Mr Ahmad fills three petrol cans at a garage, one holds
   5.1 litres, the second 4.8 litres and the third 5.2 litres.
   How much petrol does he buy?

John is 1.58 m tall. His sister Anne is 0.33 m shorter.

How tall is Anne?

Anne's height is 1.58 − 0.33 = 1.25 m or 1 m 25 cm.

**1** A bakery sells these cakes and pastries.

| Cherry bun | Danish pastry | Gingerbread man | Slice of choc fudge cake | Choc brownie |
|---|---|---|---|---|
| 49p | £1.25 | 85p | £2.30 | 99p |

Use your calculator to work out the cost of each of these orders.

**a** 3 cherry buns and a Danish pastry

**b** 1 chocolate brownie, 2 gingerbread men and a cherry bun

**c** 2 slices of chocolate fudge cake and 2 gingerbread men

**d** A Danish pastry, a gingerbread man and 2 slices of chocolate fudge cake.

**2** Use a calculator to work out these questions. Make a mental estimate for each one.

**a** 4.6 + 3.52 − 2.7    **b** 18.6 − (4.5 − 1.93)

**c** 5.9 − 2.2 + 3.15    **d** 28.4 − (2.7 + 7.95)

**e** 35.9 − 16.25 − 4.08    **f** 19.24 − (6.3 − 1.89)

**3** Sada records how much time she spends on her homework for each night one week. Copy and complete the table.

| Day | Time (hours and minutes) | Time (hours) |
|---|---|---|
| Monday | 1 hour 45 minutes (or 105 minutes) | $\frac{105}{60}$ = 1.75 hours |
| Tuesday | 1 hour 20 minutes | |
| Wednesday | 1 hour 15 minutes | |
| Thursday | 1 hour 10 minutes | |
| Friday | 1 hour 30 minutes | |

Find her total time for the week in    **a** hours    and    **b** minutes.

**MyMaths**.co.uk

# 2a Length

**Example**

The length of a Ford Focus five-door car is 4342 mm.
What is this length in    **a**   cm      **b**   m?

**a**   To convert mm to cm divide by 10 so 4342 ÷ 10 = 434.2 cm.
**b**   To convert cm to m divide by 100 so 434.2 cm ÷ 100 = 4.342 m.

---

**1**   | millimetre |    | centimetre |    | metre |    | kilometre |

   Choose the most appropriate unit to measure
   **a**   the height of a door
   **b**   the distance between two towns
   **c**   the length of a mobile phone
   **d**   the length of a beetle
   **e**   the height of a tree.

**2**   Measure the lengths of these lines in   **i** centimetres   **ii** millimetres.
   **a** _____
   **b** _____
   **c** _____

**3**   Convert these measurements to the units given.
   **a**   5 cm to mm              **b**   7 m to cm
   **c**   30 mm to cm            **d**   8000 m to km
   **e**   10.5 cm to mm         **f**   280 cm to m
   **g**   3.25 km to m           **h**   4.9 m to cm

**4**   **a**   The distance between Malpas and Tilston is 5.1 km.
       What is this distance in   **i**   m     **ii**   cm?
   **b**   The length of an Aston Martin Vanquish S is 4672 mm.
       What is this length in   **i**   cm     **ii**   m?

Write the reading on these scales.

a

b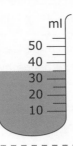

- - - - - - - - - - - - - - - - - - - - - - - - - - - - - - - - - - - - - -

**a** The arrow is pointing to 15.4 cm

**b** The volume of liquid is 35 ml.

**1** Write the reading on each of these scales.

a

b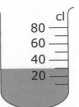

c

**2** Estimate the reading on each of these scales.

a

b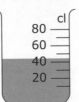

c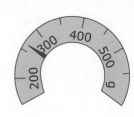

MyMaths.co.uk

# 2c Converting between metric units

**Example**

Find the perimeter of this mirror in
a   centimetres        b   metres.

1 m 5 cm

60 cm

---

a   1 m = 100 cm
So 1 m 5 cm = 105 cm
The perimeter in centimetres is
105 cm + 60 cm + 105 cm + 60 cm = 330 cm

b   330 cm = 330 ÷ 100 m = 3.3 m

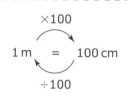

×100

1 m   =   100 cm

÷100

---

**1**   Calculate
   **a**   17 × 10        **b**   8 × 100        **c**   35 ÷ 10        **d**   4200 ÷ 100
   **e**   4.6 × 100      **f**   9.2 × 10       **g**   250 ÷ 1000     **h**   825 ÷ 100

**2**   Convert these measurements to the units given.
   **a**   14 m into cm           **b**   85 cm into mm
   **c**   6 litres into ml       **d**   7.5 litres into cl
   **e**   1.25 kg into g         **f**   25 cl into ml
   **g**   10.5 km into m         **h**   0.95 kg into g

**3**   Convert these measurements to the units given.
   **a**   500 cm into m          **b**   70 mm into cm
   **c**   3500 ml into litres    **d**   280 cl into litres
   **e**   5400 g into kg         **f**   99 ml into cl
   **g**   6250 m into km         **h**   375 g into kg

**4**   **a**   An apple weighs 250 g. Apples are sold in bags of 5.
         What is the mass of a bag of apples in   **i**   g      **ii**   kg?
   **b**   Moggie grows a sunflower that is 0.97 m tall.
         Ben grows a sunflower that is 112 cm tall.
         How much taller is Ben's sunflower?
   **c**   Calculate the perimeter of this mirror in
         **i**   centimetres      **ii**   metres.

110 cm

0.75 m

**MyMaths**.co.uk

Q 1091   **SEARCH**        **Geometry and measures**   Measures, perimeter and area

Find the perimeter of this triangle.

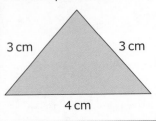

3 cm    3 cm

4 cm

3 + 3 + 4 = 10

Perimeter = 10 cm

**1** Find the perimeter of each of these rectangles.

**a**    5 cm

3 cm    3 cm

5 cm

**b**    3.9 cm

8.2 cm    8.2 cm

3.9 cm

**c**    27 mm

14 mm    14 mm

27 mm

**2** Find the perimeter of each of these triangles.

**a**

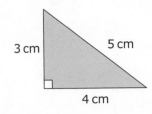

3 cm    5 cm

4 cm

**b**

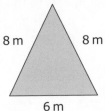

8 m    8 m

6 m

**c**

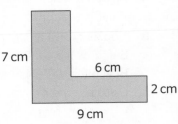

67 mm

38 mm

42 mm

**3** This shape is made from rectangles.
Find the perimeter of this shape.

7 cm

6 cm

2 cm

9 cm

**4** Find the missing lengths on
this isosceles triangle.

Perimeter = 20 m

5 m

**MyMaths**.co.uk

Q 1110    SEARCH

# 2e Area

**Example**

Calculate the area of this shape.

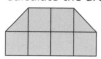

$6 + \frac{1}{2} + \frac{1}{2} = 7$ units²

**1**

| square millimetre | square centimetre | square metre | square kilometre |

Choose the most appropriate unit to measure the area of
**a** the front cover of this book
**b** a leaf from a sycamore tree
**c** your school playing field
**d** Lake Garda in Italy
**e** your thumbnail.

**2** Find the area of these shapes.

**a**   **b** 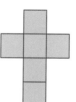  **c**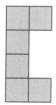

**3** Find the area of these shapes. (Remember that each triangle counts as half of a square.)

**a**   **b** 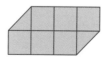  **c**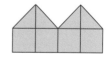

**4** On square grid paper, draw three rectangles which each have an area of 18 square centimetres.

**5** On square grid paper, draw two rectangles and one square which each have an area of 16 square centimetres.

**Example**

Find the length and perimeter of this rectangle.

?

Area = 800 cm²    16 cm

---

Area = length × width so, Length = $\frac{\text{area}}{\text{width}}$

Length = $\frac{800}{16}$ = 50 cm

Perimeter = 16 + 50 + 16 + 50 = 132 cm

**1**   **i**   Find the area of each of these shapes. What do you notice?

     **ii**   Find the perimeter of each of these shapes. What do you notice?

**a**   6 cm

24 cm

**b**   16 cm

9 cm

**c**   12 cm

12 cm

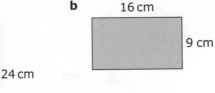
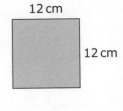

**2**   Find the area of each of these shapes.

**a**   8 mm

18 mm

4 mm

20 mm

**b**   9 cm

3 cm

6 cm

3 cm    4 cm

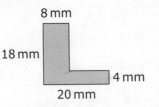
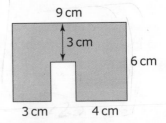

**3**   **a**   Calculate the missing lengths.

     **i**   Area = 40 cm²   ?

       10 cm

     **ii**   Area = 16 m²   ?

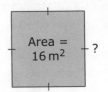

     **b**   Calculate the perimeter of each shape in part **a**.

# 2g Area of a triangle

Calculate the area of this triangle.

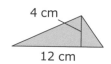

Area of triangle = $\frac{1}{2}$ × base × height

$= \frac{1}{2} × 12 × 4 = 24\,cm^2$

1 For each diagram
   i find the area of the rectangle
   ii find the area of the shaded triangle.

   **a**
   6 cm
   5 cm

   **b**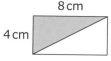
   8 cm
   4 cm

   **c**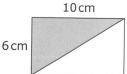
   10 cm
   6 cm

2 Calculate the area of each of these triangles.

   **a**
   5 cm
   8 cm

   **b**
   8 cm
   8 cm

   **c**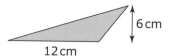
   6 cm
   12 cm

   **d**
   2.5 cm
   4 cm

   **e**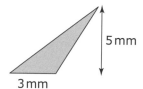
   5 mm
   3 mm

   **f**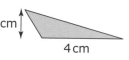
   1.5 cm
   4 cm

**Example**

Calculate the area of this parallelogram.

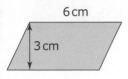

6 cm

3 cm

- - - - - - - - - - - - - - - - - - - - - - - - - - - - - - - - - - - - - - - - - - -

Area $= b \times h$

$\quad = 6\,\text{cm} \times 3\,\text{cm}$

$\quad = 18\,\text{cm}^2$

**1** Calculate the area of these parallelograms by counting squares.

**a** 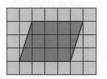  **b** 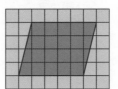  **c**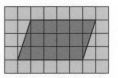

**2** Calculate the area of these parallograms by using the formula.

**a** 3.5 cm  **b** 3 cm  **c**

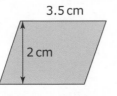
2 cm

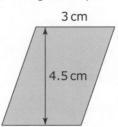
4.5 cm

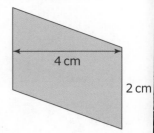
4 cm
2 cm

**3** Jonny worked out the area of this parallelogram, but he has made a mistake.

What did Jonny do wrong?

Area $= b \times h$

$\quad = 5\,\text{cm} \times 3\,\text{cm} = 15\,\text{cm}^2$

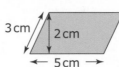
3 cm   2 cm
← 5 cm →

**MyMaths**.co.uk

Q 1108  **SEARCH**

$x$ students go to Charmaine's school. One hundred more go to Marlon's and only one third as many go to Natalie's. How many students go to

**a** Marlon's school      **b** Natalie's school?

---

**a** $x$ add 100 or $x + 100$      **b** One third of $x$ or $\dfrac{x}{3}$

**1** A coach can carry $m$ passengers.
Use symbols to write the number of people on
   **a** a coach with 5 empty seats
   **b** two full coaches
   **c** a coach that is only half full.

**2** A school hall contains $n$ chairs.
Use symbols to write the number of people
in this school hall if
   **a** 12 seats are empty
   **b** all seats are occupied and 5 people are standing at the back
   **c** $\dfrac{1}{3}$ of the seats are empty.

**3** A farmer puts $x$ sheep into each of his fields.
Use symbols to write the number of sheep
   **a** in five fields
   **b** in these five fields if the farmer adds one more sheep to **each** field
   **c** in $y$ fields.

**a** What is the length of the string of sausages?

$m$ cm

**b** What will the length be if three sausages are cut off?

- - - - - - - - - - - - - - - - - - - - - - - - - - - - - - - - - - - - -

**a** Length = $7 \times m$ or $7m$ centimetres.

**b** If three are cut off, the length of the remaining
four is $7m - 3m = 4m$ centimetres.

**1** These shapes are made from straws. Find the
perimeter of each one.

**a**

$p$ cm

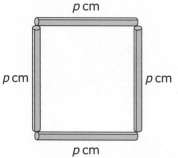

$p$ cm        $p$ cm

$p$ cm

**b**

$q$ cm

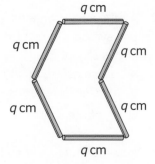

$q$ cm      $q$ cm

$q$ cm      $q$ cm

$q$ cm

**c**

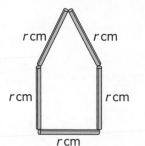

$r$ cm     $r$ cm

$r$ cm     $r$ cm

$r$ cm

**2** Simplify each expression.

| | | | |
|---|---|---|---|
| **a** | $4x + 5x$ | **b** $12z + 8z$ | **c** $3p + 5p + 7p$ |
| **d** | $9r + 10r + r$ | **e** $15n - 9n$ | **f** $10v - v$ |
| **g** | $9y + 4y - 3y$ | **h** $7p + p - 5p$ | **i** $20r - 7r - 3r$ |

# 3c    Collecting like terms

**Example**

First class stamps cost *x* pence each and second class stamps cost *y* pence each.

What is the cost of

**a**  2 first class stamps and 3 second class stamps

**b**  3 first class stamps and one second class stamp?

- - - - - - - - - - - - - - - - - - - - - - - - - - - - -

**a**  2*x* + 3*y* pence

**b**  3*x* + *y* pence

---

**1**  Write the perimeter of each shape.

**a**
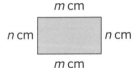

**b**

**c**
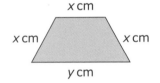

**d**
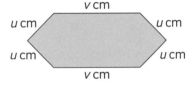

**2**  Theatre tickets are £*m* for adults and £*n* for children.
Find the cost of going to this theatre for these families.

**a**  The Jones family, 2 adults and 4 children

**b**  The Ahmad family, 2 adults and 6 children

**c**  The Brown family, 3 adults and 2 children.

**d**  Later the Brown family go again but bring Grandma Brown. How much will they have to pay now?

**3**  Simplify these expressions.

**a**  2*x* + 4*x* + 3*y*

**b**  7*u* + 5*v* + *u*

**c**  10*p* − *p* + 6*q*

**d**  15*u* − 9*v* − *u*

**e**  5*z* + 6*t* + 3*z* + 3*t*

**f**  8*m* + 7*n* − 2*m* − 3*n*

**g**  5*a* + 10*b* − 5*a* − 3*b*

**h**  9*r* − 3*s* − 4*r* + 10*s*

**i**  5*x* − 2*y* − 5*x* + 7*y*

**j**  3*m* + 9*n* + 4*m* − 5*n*

**k**  7*t* − 3*z* + 8*t* + 11

**l**  6 + 8*k* − 2 − *k*

Q 1179    **SEARCH**

**Algebra**  Expressions and formulae    **17**

Example

The formula that converts kilograms to grams is

$g = 1000 \times k$

where $g$ is the number of grams and $k$ is the number of kilograms.

Use this formula to convert these masses into grams.

**a**   3.5 kg

**b**   0.6 kg

- - - - - - - - - - - - - - - - - - - - - - - - - - - - - - - - - - - - - - - - - -

**a**   $g = 1000 \times k$
   $= 1000 \times 3.5$
   $= 3500$
   So 3.5 kg = 3500 g

**b**   $g = 1000 \times k$
   $= 1000 \times 0.6$
   $= 600$
   So 0.6 kg = 600 g

**1**   The formula that converts metres to centimetres is
   $c = 100 \times m$, where c is centimetres and $m$ is metres.
   Use this formula to convert each measurement to centimetres.
   **a**   4 m      **b**   21 m      **c**   1.5 m      **d**   0.7 m

**2**   A factory makes doors which have three hinges.
   The formula connecting hinges to doors is $h = 3 \times d$, where $h$ is
   the number of hinges and $d$ is the number of doors.
   Use this formula to find how many hinges will be
   required for
   **a**   5 doors      **b**   10 doors      **c**   25 doors      **d**   20 doors.

**3**   A taxi driver charges £5 for a call-out and then £1 for every kilometre
   travelled.
   Use the formula
   $c = n + 5$
   where $c$ is the cost in pounds and $n$ is the number of kilometres travelled
   to find the cost of travelling
   **a**   3 km      **b**   4 km      **c**   10 km      **d**   15 km.

Tickets for a football match cost £15.

**a** Write a formula for the cost, $c$, of buying $n$ tickets.

**b** Use your formula to find the cost of buying 6 tickets.

- - - - - - - - - - - - - - - - - - - - - - - - - - - - - - - - - - - - - - -

**a** $c = 15 \times n$ or $c = 15n$

**b** $c = 15n = 15 \times 6$

$c = £90$

**1** Ravinda goes for a long walk and she notices that it takes her 1 hour to walk 3 miles.

**a** Copy and complete the mapping.

| Hours | Miles |
|-------|-------|
| 1 | 3 |
| 2 | ☐ |
| 4 | ☐ |
| 7 | ☐ |

**b** Write a formula to calculate the distance that she walks.
Use $d$ for distance and $t$ for time; $d = ☐ \times t$.

**c** Use your formula to find how far she will have walked after

**i** 3 hours **ii** 5 hours **iii** 6 hours **iv** 8 hours.

**2** Isla's parents give her £5 per week and £2 for each household chore that she completes.

**a** Copy and complete this table.

| Chores completed | Amount earned | Weekly money | Total pocket money |
|------------------|---------------|--------------|--------------------|
| 1 | 1 × £2 = £2 | £5 | £7 |
| 2 | | £5 | |
| 3 | | | |

**b** Copy and complete this sentence:
'To work out Isla's pocket money you ☐ the number of chores completed by 2 and ☐ £5.'

**c** Write a formula to calculate Isla's pocket money, $P$, based on the number of chores, $c$, that she completes.

**Example**

A bread delivery man has a tray of weight 700g. He is using it to deliver loaves which weigh 500g each.

**a** Write a formula connecting $w$, the total weight that he is carrying, to $n$, the number of loaves on the tray.

**b** Use your formula to find the total weight that he is carrying if there are 5 loaves on the tray.

- - - - - - - - - - - - - - - - - - - - - - - - - - - - - - - - - -

**a** $w = 700 + 500n$

**b** $w = 700 + 500 \times 5 = 700 + 2500 = 3200\,g$

**1** The number of pencils in each of these pencil tins is $p$.

   **a** Use $p$ to write a formula for the total number of pencils $t$ in each case.

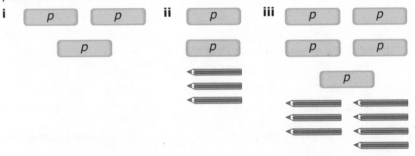

   **b** If $p = 5$, write the total number of pencils in each case.

**2** The number of jaffa cakes in each of these boxes is $c$. There are also some loose jaffa cakes.

Using $c$ for the number of cakes in each box and $t$ for the total number of cakes, write a formula for the total, $t$.

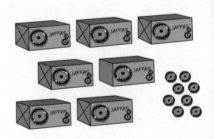

**MyMaths**.co.uk

Q 1158   **SEARCH**

# 4a Fractions

| | |
|---|---|
| Write the fraction of this circle that is shaded.<br>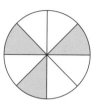 | Three equal parts out of eight are shaded, so the fraction shaded is $\frac{3}{8}$ |

**1** Write the fraction of each circle that is shaded.

**a**    **b** 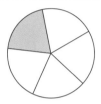   **c**

**d**    **e** 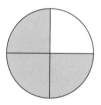   **f**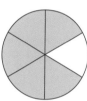

**2** What fraction of £1 (100p) is
   **a** 23p        **b** 41p        **c** 59p?

**3** What fraction of 1 hour (60 minutes) is
   **a** 19 minutes     **b** 37 minutes     **c** 41 minutes?

**4** There are 30 teachers at Mary's school and 19 of them are men. What fraction of them are
   **a** men        **b** women?

**5** A London Tube line is 40 km long of which 17 km is underground. For what fraction of its length is it
   **a** underground     **b** in the open?

**Example**

Write the fraction $\frac{3}{12}$ in its simplest form.

Divide both the numerator and the denominator by 3.

$$\frac{3}{12} = \frac{1}{4}$$

1  Giving your answer in its simplest form, write the fraction of this rectangle that is shaded.

   **a**  white

   **b**  black

   **c**  grey.

2  Copy and complete these fraction equivalents.

   **a**  $\frac{1}{3} = \frac{\square}{9}$      **b**  $\frac{3}{4} = \frac{15}{\square}$      **c**  $\frac{\square}{9} = \frac{20}{36}$      **d**  $\frac{5}{\square} = \frac{40}{48}$

3  Copy and complete these equivalent fraction families.

   **a**  $\frac{2}{5} = \frac{\square}{10} = \frac{8}{\square} = \frac{\square}{25} = \frac{20}{\square}$      **b**  $\frac{5}{8} = \frac{\square}{16} = \frac{15}{\square} = \frac{\square}{40} = \frac{40}{\square}$

4  Express these fractions in their simplest form.

   **a**  $\frac{9}{18}$      **b**  $\frac{10}{15}$      **c**  $\frac{12}{16}$      **d**  $\frac{20}{35}$      **e**  $\frac{30}{36}$

5  Calculate each of these giving your answer as a fraction in its simplest form.

   **a**  $\frac{3}{7} + \frac{1}{7}$      **b**  $\frac{8}{9} - \frac{5}{9}$      **c**  $\frac{1}{6} + \frac{5}{6}$      **d**  $\frac{9}{10} - \frac{7}{10}$

6  Jason sets off from home to school and walks for $\frac{8}{15}$ km. He then realises that he is late and runs for the remaining $\frac{7}{15}$ km to his school. How far is it from his house to his school?

MyMaths.co.uk

Q 1042  SEARCH

**Example**

Work out

**a** $\dfrac{5}{12} + \dfrac{1}{4}$ **b** $\dfrac{7}{10} - \dfrac{1}{4}$

Simplify your answer where possible.

- - - - - - - - - - - - - - - - - - - - - - - - - - - - - - - - - - - -

**a** $\dfrac{5}{12} + \dfrac{1}{4}$

Write each fraction with a common denominator.

$\overset{\times 3}{\dfrac{1}{4} = \dfrac{3}{12}}$   $\dfrac{5}{12} + \dfrac{3}{12} = \dfrac{8}{12} = \dfrac{2}{3}$
$\underset{\times 3}{}$   $\underset{\div 4}{}$

**b** $\dfrac{7}{10} - \dfrac{1}{4}$

Write each fraction with a common denominator.

$\overset{\times 2}{\dfrac{7}{10} = \dfrac{14}{20}}$   $\overset{\times 5}{\dfrac{1}{4} = \dfrac{5}{20}}$
$\underset{\times 2}{}$   $\underset{\times 5}{}$

$\dfrac{14}{20} - \dfrac{5}{20} = \dfrac{9}{20}$

**1** Add these fractions.
Simplify where possible.

**a** $\dfrac{5}{8} + \dfrac{2}{8}$ **b** $\dfrac{3}{10} + \dfrac{3}{10}$ **c** $\dfrac{1}{4} + \dfrac{2}{4}$ **d** $\dfrac{2}{3} + \dfrac{1}{6}$

**e** $\dfrac{3}{10} + \dfrac{2}{5}$ **f** $\dfrac{2}{9} + \dfrac{1}{9}$ **g** $\dfrac{1}{3} + \dfrac{1}{4}$ **h** $\dfrac{1}{12} + \dfrac{1}{6} + \dfrac{1}{4}$

**2** Subtract these fractions.
Simplify where possible.

**a** $\dfrac{6}{8} - \dfrac{2}{8}$ **b** $\dfrac{7}{10} - \dfrac{2}{10}$ **c** $\dfrac{7}{12} - \dfrac{2}{12}$ **d** $\dfrac{3}{4} - \dfrac{1}{8}$

**e** $\dfrac{8}{9} - \dfrac{1}{3}$ **f** $\dfrac{5}{6} - \dfrac{1}{6}$ **g** $\dfrac{4}{5} - \dfrac{1}{4}$ **h** $\dfrac{8}{9} - \dfrac{5}{6}$

**MyMaths**.co.uk

Q 1017   **SEARCH**

**a** Convert $\frac{3}{25}$ to a decimal.

**b** Convert 0.4 to a fraction in its simplest form.

**a** $\frac{3}{25}$ $\overset{\times 4}{=}$ $\frac{12}{100}$ which is 0.12 as a decimal. **b** $0.4 = \overset{\div 2}{\frac{4}{10}} = \frac{2}{5}$

$\times 4$ $\div 2$

**1** These fractions all have well-known decimal equivalents.
Copy and complete the table.

| Fraction | $\frac{1}{2}$ | | $\frac{1}{10}$ | $\frac{3}{4}$ | | | $\frac{1}{3}$ | |
|---|---|---|---|---|---|---|---|---|
| Decimal | | 0.25 | | | 0.01 | 0.2 | | 0.5 |

**2** Write these decimals as fractions.
  **a** 0.9    **b** 0.3    **c** 0.83    **d** 0.39    **e** 0.07

**3** Write these decimals as fractions in their simplest form.
  **a** 0.2    **b** 0.8    **c** 0.15    **d** 0.68    **e** 0.04

**4** Write these fractions as decimals using equivalent fractions.
  **a** $\frac{4}{5} = \frac{\square}{10} = 0.\square$    **b** $\frac{17}{20} = \frac{\square}{100} = 0.\square\square$
  **c** $\frac{23}{50}$    **d** $\frac{7}{25}$

**5** These are Lynda's exam results. Write them in order, beginning with the subject in which she scored the highest mark.
  English $\frac{37}{50}$    Geography $\frac{54}{40}$
  Mathematics $\frac{36}{60}$    History $\frac{54}{60}$

Hint: Use your calculator to convert the fractions to decimals and then put the decimals in order.

MyMaths.co.uk

Q 1016    SEARCH

# 4e Fraction of a quantity

Calculate $\frac{7}{12}$ of 60 cm.

First find $\frac{1}{12}$. $\qquad \frac{1}{12}$ of 60 cm = 60 cm ÷ 12

$\qquad\qquad\qquad\qquad = 5\,cm$

Then multiply by 7. $\qquad \frac{7}{12}$ of 60 cm = 5 cm × 7

$\qquad\qquad\qquad\qquad = 35\ cm$

**1** Calculate

   **a** $\frac{1}{3}$ of £90   **b** $\frac{1}{5}$ of 80 cm   **c** $\frac{1}{8}$ of 96 kg   **d** $\frac{1}{7}$ of 84 m

**2** Use your answers to question **1** to calculate these.

   **a** $\frac{2}{3}$ of £90   **b** $\frac{3}{5}$ of 80 cm   **c** $\frac{5}{8}$ of 96 kg   **d** $\frac{6}{7}$ of 84 m

**3** Calculate

   **a** $\frac{3}{8}$ of £24          **b** $\frac{4}{9}$ of 18 kg

   **c** $\frac{5}{6}$ of 30 litres    **d** $\frac{3}{7}$ of \$28

   **e** $\frac{3}{5}$ of €60        **f** $\frac{7}{10}$ of 50 m

   **g** $\frac{11}{12}$ of 96 cm    **h** $\frac{5}{16}$ of 128 MB

**4** Calculate

   **a** $5 \times \frac{1}{7}$   **b** $4 \times \frac{2}{9}$   **c** $2 \times \frac{3}{4}$   **d** $5 \times \frac{2}{3}$

**5** Peter is 150 cm tall and his sister Jane is $\frac{5}{6}$ as tall as Peter. How tall is Jane?

**6** Harry receives £30 for his birthday. He spends $\frac{2}{5}$ of his money on a DVD and $\frac{4}{15}$ on a book. Harry puts the rest in his piggy bank.

   **a** Calculate the price of the DVD.

   **b** Calculate the amount that Harry saves in his piggy bank.

**MyMaths**.co.uk

Q 1018   SEARCH

**Number** Fractions, decimals and percentages    25

Convert 86% to a decimal.

- - - - - - - - - - - - - - - - - - - - - - - - - - - - - - - - - - - - - -

$86\% = \frac{86}{100} = 0.86$

**1** Write these percentages as decimals.

    **a** 24%   **b** 19%   **c** 70%   **d** 7%    **e** 120%

**2** Write these decimals as percentages.

    **a** 0.51   **b** 0.08   **c** 0.6   **d** 0.175   **e** 1.5

**3** Write these percentages as fractions in their simplest form.

    $\div 20$

    **a** $20\% = \dfrac{\square}{100} = \dfrac{\square}{5}$     **b** $35\% = \dfrac{\square}{100} = \dfrac{\square}{\square}$

    $\div 20$                                $\div 5$

    **c** 74%                **d** 56%

**4** Write these fractions as percentages using equivalent fractions.

    $\times 25$

    **a** $\dfrac{3}{4} = \dfrac{\square}{100} = \square\%$     **b** $\dfrac{4}{5} = \dfrac{\square}{100} = \square\%$

    $\times 25$

    **c** $\dfrac{3}{20}$              **d** $\dfrac{11}{25}$

**5** Pair these cards if they show equivalent numbers.
   Which is the odd card out?

    [ 40% ]   [ 0.45 ]   [ 0.045 ]   [ 450% ]   [ 4% ]

       [ 0.4 ]   [ 4.5 ]   [ 4.5% ]   [ 45% ]

MyMaths.co.uk

Q 1015   SEARCH

# 4g  Percentages of an amount

Calculate 5% of £320.

5% of £320 = $\frac{5}{100}$ × 320      Convert to a fraction.

         = $\frac{1}{20}$ × 320      Simplify the fraction.

         = 320 ÷ 20      Multiplying by $\frac{1}{20}$ is the

         = £16           same as ÷20.

**1** Calculate these percentages using a mental method.
- **a** 50% of £60
- **b** 25% of 36 litres
- **c** 10% of 80 m
- **d** 50% of 45 cm
- **e** 25% of £150
- **f** 10% of 35 litres

**2** Calculate these percentages using a written method.
- **a** 5% of 40 kg
- **b** 30% of 120 mm
- **c** 15% of £80
- **d** 70% of 90 litres
- **e** 45% of €200
- **f** 11% of £4000

**3** A crowded bus has 80 passengers on board. 40% of them are sitting downstairs, 45% of them are sitting upstairs and the rest are standing.
- **a** Write the percentage of passengers that are standing.
- **b** Calculate the number of passengers sitting upstairs.

**4** Work out the new cost of these sale items.
- **a** trousers £40
- **b** coat £120
- **c** jumper £30
- **d** t-shirt £10

15% off all
Sale items!

**Example**

Calculate 35% of £150.

---

35% of £150 = $\frac{35}{100}$ × 150 = £52.50

**1** Write these percentages as fractions in their simplest form.

a 70% = $\frac{\square}{100}$ = $\frac{\square}{10}$  b 45% = $\frac{\square}{100}$ = $\frac{\square}{\square}$  c 7%

d 150%  e 117.5%

**2** Write these percentages as decimals.

a 70%  b 45%  c 7%  d 150%  e 117.5%

**3** Write these fractions as percentages using equivalent fractions.

a $\frac{2}{5}$ = $\frac{\square}{100}$ = $\square$ %  b $\frac{3}{10}$ = $\frac{\square}{100}$ = $\square$ %  c $\frac{19}{25}$

d $\frac{52}{40}$  e $1\frac{3}{20}$

**4** Write these fractions as decimals.

a $\frac{2}{5}$  b $\frac{13}{10}$  c $\frac{19}{25}$  d $\frac{52}{40}$  e $1\frac{3}{20}$

**5** Pair these cards if they show equivalent numbers.
Which is the odd card out?

250%  25%  20%  0.25  2.5

0.2  2.5%  0.02  2%

**6** Calculate these percentages without using a calculator.

a 50% of 60 people  b 25% of 80 cm
c 10% of £150  d 20% of 1200 g
e 75% of 40 m  f 5% of €90

**MyMaths**.co.uk

Q 1029  SEARCH

When a stopwatch ticks from zero to 15 seconds, what angle does the pointer turn through?

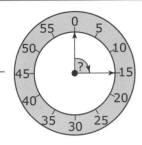

The angle is $\frac{1}{4}$ of a turn, which is $\frac{1}{4}$ of 360°, or 90°.

**1** Look at the stopwatch in the example. Copy and complete the table to show the angle that the pointer turns through.

| Time | Angle (as a fraction of a turn) | Angle (in degrees) |
|---|---|---|
| 0 to 30 seconds | $\frac{30}{60} = \frac{1}{2}$ | $\frac{1}{2} \times 360 =$ |
| 0 to 45 seconds | | |
| 0 to 20 seconds | | |
| 0 to 40 seconds | | |
| 0 to 12 seconds | | |

**2** One angle between a pair of perpendicular lines is 90°, or a right angle. What is the reflex angle between these lines?

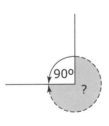

**3** Match one of these cards with each angle below.

acute      reflex      obtuse      right

a
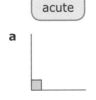

b

c

d
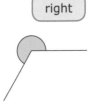

Measure angle LMN.

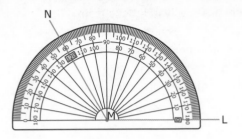

1 Place your protractor on the angle so that the cross is on M and ML is on the zero line.
2 Start from 0° at L and read where MN cuts the scale.
3 Angle LMN = 120°

1 Write down the size of each of these angles.

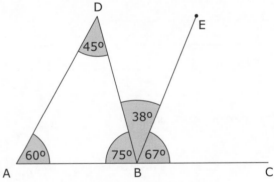

a ABD

b DBE

c DAB

d EBC

e ADB

2 Measure these angles with a protractor.

a

b

3 Work out the reflex angle for each angle in question 2.

 **MyMaths**.co.uk

Q 1081  SEARCH

Make an accurate copy of this diagram.
Join B to C and measure the length of the line.
Measure the size of each of the two
angles made.

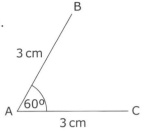

The line is 3 cm long and the two
angles are both 60°.

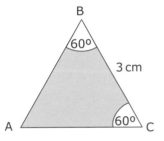

**1**  Draw these lines accurately.
Write the length of each line in millimetres.
   **a**  7.5 cm    **b**  12.4 cm    **c**  8.2 cm

**2**  Draw these angles accurately using a protractor.
Write the sizes of the reflex angles that you have also drawn.
   **a**  50°    **b**  30°    **c**  120°    **d**  115°

**3**  Make an accurate copy of each diagram. Join B to C
and measure the length of the line. Measure the
sizes of the two angles that you have made.

**a**
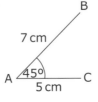

**b**
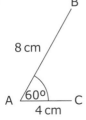

**c**
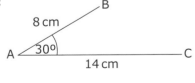

Calculate the unknown angles.

**a**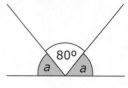

**b**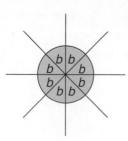

- - - - - - - - - - - - - - - - - - - - - - - - - - - - - - - - - - - - -

**a**   $180 - 80 = 100$   so $a = \frac{100}{2} = 50°$    **b**   $b = \frac{360}{8} = 45°$

**1** Calculate the unknown angles.

**a**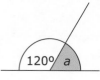

**b**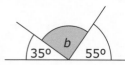

**c**

**2** Calculate the unknown angles.

**a**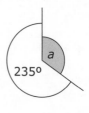

**b**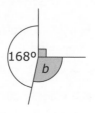

**c**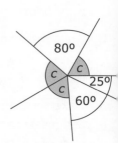

**3** Calculate the unknown angles.

**a**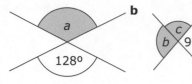

**b**

**c**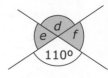

**Geometry and measures**  Angles and 2D shapes

**MyMaths**.co.uk

🔍 1082    SEARCH

Calculate the missing angle in this triangle.

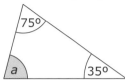

Angles in a triangle add up to 180°.

$$a + 75° + 35° = 180°$$
$$a = 70°$$

Check: $70° + 75° + 35° = 180°$

**1** Calculate the missing angles in each of these triangles.

**a**

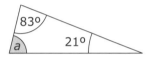

**b**

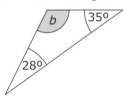

**c**

**2** Calculate the unknown angles in these isosceles triangles.

**a**

**b**

**c**

**3** Find the angles marked with letters.

**a**

**b**

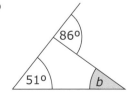

**c**

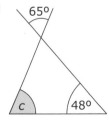

# 5f    Properties of triangles

**Example**

Write the names of the triangles from their description.
a   a triangle with no equal sides and no equal angles
b   a triangle with two equal sides and two equal angles
c   a triangle with three equal sides and three 60° angles
d   a triangle which has a right angle as one of its angles.

a   scalene     b   isosceles     c   equilateral     d   right-angled

**1** State whether each of these triangles is equilateral, isosceles, scalene or right-angled. Explain your answer.

a
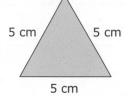
5 cm   5 cm
5 cm

b
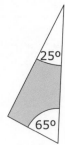
25°
65°

c
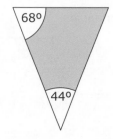
68°
44°

d
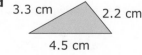
3.3 cm   2.2 cm
4.5 cm

**2** Choose two of these cards to classify each of these triangles.

scalene     equilateral     isosceles     right-angled

You may use each card more than once.

a
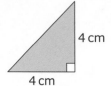
4 cm
4 cm

b
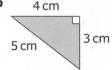
4 cm
5 cm   3 cm

MyMaths.co.uk

Q 1130    SEARCH

Here are two different-sized isosceles right-angled triangles.

Show how four of the smaller ones and two of the larger ones can be used to make a square.

**1**   Show how each of these shapes can be made from this isosceles right-angled triangle.

   **a**   a square, using two triangles

   **b**   a square, using four triangles

   **c**   a rectangle, using four triangles

   **d**   a parallelogram, using four triangles

   **e**   an isosceles right-angled triangle, using four triangles

**2**   Match these shapes with their descriptions and name each shape.

   **a**   four equal sides, opposite sides are parallel, opposite angles are equal, diagonals bisect at 90° and are different lengths

   **b**   opposite sides are parallel and equal in length, four 90° angles, diagonals bisect each other and are equal in length

   **c**   opposite sides are parallel and equal in length, opposite angles are equal, diagonals bisect each other and are different lengths

   **d**   one pair of opposite and parallel sides

Write the usual name of

**a** a regular triangle

**b** a regular quadrilateral.

- - - - - - - - - - - - - - - - - - - - - - - - - - - - - - - - -

**a** A triangle with equal sides and equal angles is an equilateral triangle.

**b** A quadrilateral with equal sides and equal angles is a square.

**1** Calculate the missing angles in these triangles.

**a**
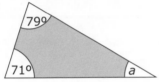

**b**
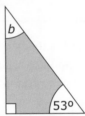

**c**
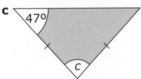

**d**

**2 a** Write the names of these regular polygons.

**i**      **ii**      **iii**

**b** Draw each shape using a ruler and a protractor.

**c** Find the interior angle of each shape.

**Example**

Give the coordinates of the three corners of this triangle.

– – – – – – – – – – – – – – – – – – – –

A is at (1, 2), B is at (−1, −2) and C is at (3, −2).

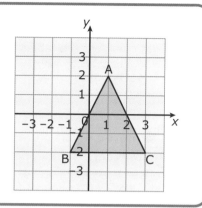

1  **a**  Write the coordinates of the points A, B and C.

  **b**  Plot a fourth point, whose x- and y-coordinates are negative, to form a parallelogram ABCD.

  **c**  Write the coordinates of D.

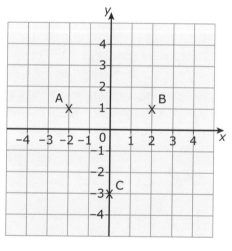

2  Draw a pair of axes with the x-axis numbered from −5 to 5 and the y-axis numbered from −10 to 10. Plot the positions of each set of points. Join each point to the next with a straight line and suggest a name for the picture.

  **a**  (1, 10), (1, 5), (2, 4), (2, −5), (1, −6), (0, −6), (−1, −5), (−1, 4), (0, 5), (0, 10), (1, 10)

  **b**  (1, 10), (1, −1), (2, 9), (3, 10), (4, 9), (4, −7), (3, −10), (3, −5), (4, −5), (3, −5), (3, 9), (2, −1), (2, −3), (−1, −3), (1, −3), (1, −7), (−1, −7), (1, −7), (0, −10), (−1, −7), (−1, −3), (−2, −3), (−2, −1), (1, −1), (−1, −1), (−1, 10), (1, 10)

**Example**

The perimeter of a square is 4 times its side length.

Copy and complete the table.

| Side length (cm) | 1.5 | 3 | 4.5 | 6 |
|---|---|---|---|---|
| Perimeter (cm) | | | | |

Side length

| Side length (cm) | 1.5 | 3 | 4.5 | 6 |
|---|---|---|---|---|
| Perimeter (cm) | 6 | 12 | 18 | 24 |

**1** The perimeter of an equilateral triangle is three times
its side length.
Copy and complete the table.

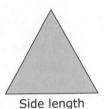

| Side length (cm) | 4 | 8 | 12 | 16 | 20 | 24 | 28 |
|---|---|---|---|---|---|---|---|
| Perimeter (cm) | | | | | | | |

Side length

**2** Rebecca is going on holiday to Barbados. She uses the formula
£1 = $4 to convert pounds to Barbados dollars. Copy and complete
this table of values.

| £ | 1 | 2 | 3 | 5 | 10 | 20 | 100 |
|---|---|---|---|---|---|---|---|
| $ | | | | | | | |

**3** If a rectangle is made from four squares,
its width is $\frac{1}{4}$ of its length.
Use this formula to complete a copy
of the table.

width = length ÷ 4

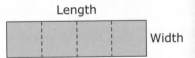

Length

Width

| Length (cm) | 8 | 10 | 12 | 14 | 16 | 18 | 20 |
|---|---|---|---|---|---|---|---|
| Width (cm) | | | | | | | |

**Example**

Kanika has gone for a long walk. The table shows how far she has gone after certain times. Plot the coordinates on the grid.

| Time (hours) | 0 | 1 | 2 | 3 | 4 |
|---|---|---|---|---|---|
| Distance (km) | 0 | 3 | 6 | 9 | 12 |

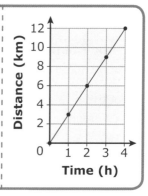

**1**   On a copy of the grid, plot the coordinates from the table and join the points with a straight line.
The first one has been done for you.

| $x$ | 0 | 1 | 2 | 3 | 4 | 5 | 6 | 7 |
|---|---|---|---|---|---|---|---|---|
| $y$ | 3 | 4 | 5 | 6 | 7 | 8 | 9 | 10 |

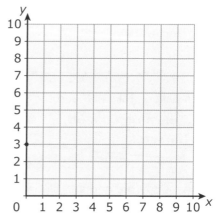

**2**   Josiah is doing an experiment by hanging weights on a spring.

   **a**   On a copy of the grid, plot his results from the table and join the points with a straight line.

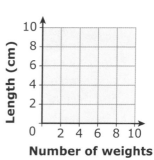

| Number of weights hanging | 2 | 4 | 6 | 8 | 10 |
|---|---|---|---|---|---|
| Length of spring (cm) | 5 | 6 | 7 | 8 | 9 |

   **b**   Extend the line back until it crosses the 'length' axis and give the coordinates of the point where the line crosses the axis.

   **c**   What does your answer to part **b** tell you?

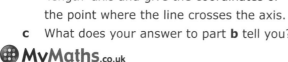

**MyMaths**.co.uk

**Algebra**   Graphs

Rebecca is jogging along a road. The table shows her progress.

| Time (minutes) | 0 (start) | 10 | 30 |
|---|---|---|---|
| Distance gone (km) | 0 | 2 | 6 |

Plot these values on a graph and join the points with a straight line. Use your graph to estimate how far she has gone after 20 minutes.

From the graph you can see that she has covered 4 km after 20 minutes.

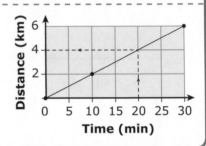

**1** A balloon takes off and the table shows its progress.

| Time after take-off (minutes) | 0 | 15 | 30 |
|---|---|---|---|
| Height reached (metres) | 0 | 90 | 180 |

a Copy the grid and plot these values. Join the points with a straight line.

b Estimate the height reached after
   i 5 minutes   ii 20 minutes.

c Estimate the time taken to reach a height of
   i 60 metres   ii 150 metres.

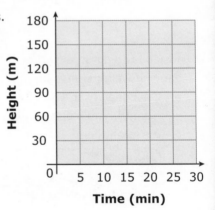

**a**  567 people live in Paul's village. Round this
number to the nearest 10.

**b**  The tripmeter in Mr Amhad's car recorded his
distance to work as 13.5 km. Round this number
to the nearest kilometre.

- - - - - - - - - - - - - - - - - - - - - - - - - - - - - - - - - - - - - - -

**a**  567 lies between 560 and 570 but is closer to 570.
So 567 rounds to 570 (nearest 10).

**b**  The 5 rounds up.
So 13.5 rounds to 14 km (nearest km).

**1**  Round these numbers to the nearest 10.

    **a**  32            **b**  89

    **c**  25            **d**  124

    **e**  1836

**2**  Round these numbers to the nearest  **i**  100 and  **ii**  1000.

    **a**  843          **b**  928

    **c**  1884        **d**  3655

    **e**  24 930

**3**  Round these numbers to the nearest tenth.

    **a**  3.21        **b**  6.78

    **c**  5.97        **d**  2.341

    **e**  9.072

**4**  Yasmin records the midday temperature (in °C) in Chester during
one week in October.

| Mon | Tue | Wed | Thu | Fri | Sat | Sun |
|------|------|------|------|------|-----|-----|
| 12.8 | 13.5 | 14.2 | 12.1 | 11.0 | 9.9 | 9.5 |

Make a table which shows the temperatures
rounded to the nearest degree.

Calculate $(15 - 3) \times 4 + 3$

---

$(15 - 3) \times 4 + 3 = 12 \times 4 + 3$     Brackets first
$= 48 + 3$     Then multiply or divide
$= 51$     Then add or subtract

**1** Use the correct order of operations to work these out.

    **a**   $2 \times 3 + 4$       **b**   $10 + 6 \div 2$

    **c**   $9 + 2 \times 6$       **d**   $20 - 5 \times 3$

    **e**   $4 \times 3 + 2 \times 5$       **f**   $21 - 8 \div 4$

    **g**   $7 + 16 \div 2$       **h**   $18 \div 2 - 12 \div 3$

**2** Calculate

    **a**   $3 \times (4 + 2)$       **b**   $(12 - 5) \div 7$

    **c**   $(22 - 10) \times 2$       **d**   $20 \div (9 - 4)$

**3** Calculate

    **a**   $\dfrac{18 + 9}{3}$       **b**   $\dfrac{30 - 16}{2}$

    **c**   $\dfrac{40}{3 + 5}$       **d**   $\dfrac{54}{4 + 5}$

**4** Calculate

    **a**   $(18 + 7) \times (11 + 9)$

    **b**   $(100 - 65) \times (12 + 8)$

    **c**   $6 \times (17 + 13) \times 5$

    **d**   $(135 - 15) \div (7 + 13)$

**5** Copy these calculations and insert brackets, if necessary, to make the answers correct.

    **a**   $4 \times 6 + 5 = 44$

    **b**   $8 + 12 \div 2 = 10$

    **c**   $60 - 45 \div 9 = 55$

    **d**   $4 \times 2 + 5 \times 6 = 38$

**MyMaths**.co.uk

  1167   SEARCH

**Example**

Work out 9 × 17 by    **a** partitioning    **b** compensation.

**a**   9 × 17 = 9 × 10 + 9 × 7 = 90 + 63 = 153

**b**   9 × 17 = 10 × 17 − 1 × 17 = 170 − 17 = 153

**1** Use multiplication facts to copy and complete these calculations.

   **a**   4 × 8 = ☐      **b**   9 × 5 = ☐

   **c**   4 × ☐ = 24      **d**   ☐ × 7 = 21

   **e**   ☐ × 6 = 48      **f**   ☐ × 9 = 63

   **g**   7 × 7 = ☐      **h**   ☐ × 8 = 72

**2** Calculate these mentally using question **1** to help you.

   **a**   40 × 8      **b**   9 × 50

   **c**   800 × 6      **d**   70 × 70

   **e**   210 ÷ 3      **f**   240 ÷ 6

   **g**   6300 ÷ 9      **h**   720 ÷ 80

**3** Calculate these using the method of partitioning.

   **a**   8 × 14      **b**   7 × 18      **c**   15 × 14      **d**   12 × 17

   **e**   75 ÷ 5      **f**   125 ÷ 5      **g**   396 ÷ 3      **h**   324 ÷ 4

**4** Calculate these using the method of compensation.

   **a**   16 × 9      **b**   23 × 9      **c**   9 × 19      **d**   19 × 12

   **e**   29 × 11      **f**   15 × 39      **g**   59 × 20      **h**   17 × 99

**5** Use an **appropriate** method to solve these.

   **a**   Claudia buys 5 bars of soap at 80p each.
How much does she spend?

   **b**   A train consists of 6 coaches. Each coach is filled to capacity with 59 passengers. How many passengers are travelling on the train?

   **c**   Bruce is asked to set out 19 rows of 22 chairs for assembly.
How many chairs must he put out?

   **d**   A small school has 5 classes of equal size. There are 135 students in the school. Find the number of students in each class.

**Example**

Use the grid method to calculate 13 × 24

Estimate: 13 × 24 ≈ 10 × 20 = 200

| × | 20 | 4 |
|---|-----|---|
| 10 | 10 × 20 = 200 | 10 × 4 = 40 |
| 3 | 3 × 20 = 60 | 3 × 4 = 12 |

200 + 60 + 40 + 12 = 312

1   Copy and complete each grid and work out these calculations. Remember to add up the four sections of the grid to get your answer.

a   15 × 21

| × | 20 | 1 |
|---|-----|---|
| 10 | 10 × 20 = 200 | |
| 5 | | |

b   14 × 32

| × | 30 | 2 |
|---|-----|---|
| 10 | | |
| 4 | 4 × 30 = 120 | |

c   28 × 43

| × | 40 | 3 |
|---|-----|---|
| 20 | | |
| 8 | | |

d   32 × 59

| × | 30 | 2 |
|---|-----|---|
| 50 | | |
| 9 | | |

2   Calculate these using a written method of your choice.
Remember to estimate first.
a   11 × 19          b   16 × 18
c   13 × 26          d   29 × 31
e   45 × 66          f   53 × 78
g   19 × 108         h   35 × 264

3   Mr Green has to travel 27 km to work. If he makes the journey 12 times a week, find the total distance that he has to commute.

**Example**

Calculate 364 ÷ 15

$$
\begin{array}{r}
24 \\
15{\overline{)364}} \\
\end{array}
$$

$-300 \leftarrow 15 \times \textcircled{2} = 30$

$\phantom{-3}64$

$\phantom{-3}-60 \leftarrow 15 \times \textcircled{4} = 60$

$\phantom{-3}\phantom{-6}4 \quad$ So 364 ÷ 15 = 24 r 4

1    Calculate these division questions.
   a   84 ÷ 7        b   96 ÷ 6        c   108 ÷ 4
   d   154 ÷ 11      e   208 ÷ 16

2    Calculate these using an appropriate method.
   a   91 ÷ 13       b   180 ÷ 15
   c   198 ÷ 18      d   238 ÷ 14
   e   255 ÷ 17      f   294 ÷ 21
   g   768 ÷ 32      h   966 ÷ 42

3    Calculate these using an appropriate method.
     Give each answer with a remainder.
   a   124 ÷ 12      b   198 ÷ 16
   c   298 ÷ 14      d   355 ÷ 15
   e   369 ÷ 23      f   780 ÷ 37
   g   1290 ÷ 45     h   1645 ÷ 52

4    a   A pipeline is to be laid from a village to a reservoir
         which is 990 metres away. If the pipes are each 15 metres
         long, how many will be required?
     b   Ellie uses 14 litres of petrol driving from London to Birmingham. She
         travels 196 kilometres. How far does Ellie travel on one litre of petrol?
     c   Ruby shares a lottery win of £1824 between herself and 11 members
         of her family. How much does each person receive?

**MyMaths**.co.uk

Q 1041    SEARCH

Use your calculator to work out $1.5 \times (30 - 3) \div 0.9$

$\boxed{1}\,\boxed{.}\,\boxed{5}\,\boxed{\times}\,\boxed{(}\,\boxed{3}\,\boxed{0}\,\boxed{-}\,\boxed{3}\,\boxed{)}\,\boxed{\div}\,\boxed{0}\,\boxed{.}\,\boxed{9}\,\boxed{=}\quad \boxed{45}$

**1** Use a calculator to work out these.

　**a** $9 \times 4 + 8 \times 3$　　　**b** $4.8 \div 0.6 + 40 \times 0.7$

　**c** $0.7 \times 30 - 3 \div 0.5$　　**d** $3 \times (4 + 3) \times 4$

　**e** $56 \div (3 + 4) \times 3$　　**f** $9.6 \div (0.6 + 0.2) \div 4$

**2** Use a scientific calculator to work out these.

　**a** $(24 + 52) \times 18$　　　**b** $2065 \div (89 - 54)$

　**c** $93 \times (51 - 23)$　　　**d** $\dfrac{1248}{30 + 18}$

　**e** $\dfrac{15.6}{13} + 9.4$　　　**f** $\dfrac{77.8 - 32.7}{8.2}$

**3** Use a calculator to solve these problems, giving your answers in a form appropriate to the question.

　**a** Flora's parents hire a 'playbarn' at a cost of £184 for their daughter's birthday party. Flora invites 15 friends. How much do her parents pay per head?

　**b** A garden centre manager has 400 kg of compost. If he packs an equal amount into 16 bags, how many kilograms of compost are there in each bag?

　**c** A pack of 12 jaffa cakes costs £0.75. Work out the cost of one jaffa cake.

　**d** An apple weighs 250 g. A bag of organic apples costs £2.00 for 1.5 kg. How much does one apple cost?

MyMaths.co.uk

Q 1167　　SEARCH

**Example**

The bar chart shows the different types of coffee sold between 2 p.m. and 3 p.m. on a particular Monday.

a  Which was the most popular type of coffee?

b  Transfer the information on this bar chart into a table.

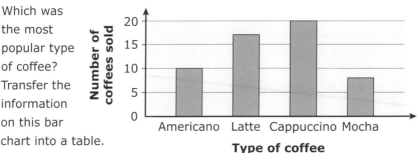

**Type of coffee**

- - - - - - - - - - - - - - - - - - - - - - - - - - - - - - - -

a  Cappuccino

b

| Type of coffee | Americano | Latte | Cappuccino | Mocha |
|---|---|---|---|---|
| Frequency | 10 | 17 | 20 | 8 |

**1** This table shows the number of letters in the first twenty-five words of 'Harry Potter and the Philosopher's Stone' by J.K. Rowling.

| Number of letters | 1 | 2 | 3 | 4 | 5 | 6 | 7 | 8 | 9 |
|---|---|---|---|---|---|---|---|---|---|
| Frequency | 0 | 3 | 5 | 9 | 3 | 3 | 1 | 0 | 1 |

Draw a bar chart to show this data.

**2** The bar chart shows the number of goals that a school football team scored in each of their matches one season.

a  Copy and complete the table.

| Number of goals scored | 0 | 1 | 2 | 3 | 4 |
|---|---|---|---|---|---|
| Number of times | | | | | |

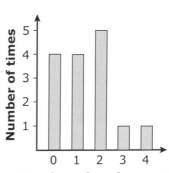

**Number of goals scored**

b  How many matches did this team play in?

c  Work out the total number of goals scored this season.

The pie chart shows in which of two cars
passengers on a tram are seated.

**a**   Write the fraction seated in the second car.

**b**   18 people are seated in the second car.
Work out the total number of people on
the tram.

**c**   How many people are seated in the first car?

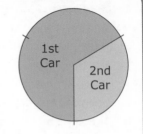

**a**   $\frac{1}{3}$

**b**   $\frac{1}{3}$ represents 18 people so 18 × 3 = 54 people on the tram

**c**   $\frac{2}{3}$ of 54 = 36 people in the first car

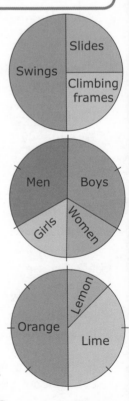

**1**   The pie chart shows how 60 children
are playing in a park.

  **a**   What fraction are playing on each
piece of equipment?

  **b**   What percentage are playing on each?

  **c**   How many children are playing on each?

**2**   There are 48 passengers on a bus.
The pie chart shows how many are men,
women, boys and girls.

  **a**   What fraction of each are there?

  **b**   How many of each are there?

**3**   A school tuck shop sells cups of squash.
The pie chart shows the flavours sold during
one break time.

  **a**   The tuck shop sold 15 cups of lemon
squash. Work out the total number of cups
of squash sold.

  **b**   Calculate the number of cups of lime squash sold.

⊞ **MyMaths**.co.uk

Q 1206   **SEARCH**

# 8c    Line graphs

Joanna placed a large jar outside her house on a wet morning and measured the depth of water in the jar at hourly intervals. The data are shown on the graph.

**a** Estimate the depth of the water at 9.30 a.m.

**b** At what time must the rain have stopped?

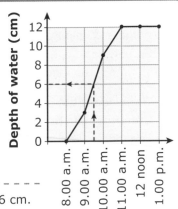

- - - - - - - - - - - - - - - - - - - - - - - - - - - - -

**a** The depth of the water at 9.30 a.m. is 6 cm.

**b** The rain stopped at around 11.00 a.m. as the depth stopped increasing.

**1** The table shows the number of people in a coffee bar over the course of one particular Monday.

| Time | 09:00 | 10:00 | 11:00 | 12:00 | 13:00 | 14:00 | 15:00 | 16:00 | 17:00 |
|------|-------|-------|-------|-------|-------|-------|-------|-------|-------|
| Number of people | 5 | 6 | 12 | 15 | 20 | 9 | 15 | 8 | 4 |

**a** Draw a line graph for this data.

**b** Describe the main features of the graph, giving possible reasons for the differences.

**2** The table shows the temperature in °C taken at hourly intervals throughout Sunday, 8 July 2007, in Wick and Camborne.

| | 10:00 | 11:00 | 12:00 | 13:00 | 14:00 | 15:00 | 16:00 | 17:00 |
|------|-------|-------|-------|-------|-------|-------|-------|-------|
| **Wick** | 12 | 13 | 13 | 14 | 14 | 14 | 15 | 15 |
| **Camborne** | 17 | 17 | 15 | 16 | 16 | 15 | 17 | 16 |

**a** On the same set of axes, plot line graphs for this data.

**b** Describe the behaviour of the temperature in Wick and Camborne on 8 July 2007.

**MyMaths**.co.uk

Q 1198    **SEARCH**

Peter always arrives at school before his classes begin. These times are the number of minutes early that Peter arrived over one week.

5, 3, 4, 2, 5

Find     **a**   the mode     **b**   the median     **c**   the range.

- - - - - - - - - - - - - - - - - - - - - - - - - - - - - - - - - - - - -

**a**   The mode is the most common result. The mode is 5 minutes.

**b**   Order the data to give 2, 3, 4, 5, 5 and choose the middle result.
The median is 4 minutes.

**c**   The range is 5 − 2 = 3 minutes

**1**   For each set of data, find

    **i**   the mode     **ii**   the median     **iii**   the range.

    **a**   9, 7, 2, 7, 4

    **b**   3, 5, 6, 2, 4, 3, 5, 1, 7

    **c**   15, 12, 18, 13, 17, 15

    **d**   102, 108, 101, 104, 108, 109

**2**   Clara throws a tetrahedron-shaped dice.
The table shows her scores.

| Score | 1 | 2 | 3 | 4 |
|---|---|---|---|---|
| Frequency | 4 | 3 | 9 | 4 |

    **a**   Write the modal score.

    **b**   Do you think this is a fair dice?
Give reasons for your answer.

**3**   Freya recorded the times in which she ran a 100 m sprint in her last athletics season.
Unfortunately she lost one of her times.
Find two possible times from the information given.

| 13.9 | 14.2 | 13.8 | 14.1 | ? |

Range = 0.5 seconds

Josiah gets the same bus to work six days a week.
One week his journey times were
12, 10, 15, 10, 12 and 10 minutes.
Find   **a**   the mode   **b**   the median   **c**   the mean of these times.

---

**a**   The mode is 10 minutes, because this time occurred more
frequently than any other.

**b**   The six times arranged in order are 10, 10, 10, 12, 12 and
15 minutes. So the median is 11 minutes, the middle number
between the third and fourth terms.

**c**   The total of the times is 12 + 10 + 15 + 10 + 12 + 10 = 69
So the mean is 69 ÷ 6 = 11.5 minutes.

**1**   Find the mean of each of these sets of numbers.

    **a**   6, 9, 10, 11

    **b**   11, 12, 15, 18, 13, 16, 10, 19

    **c**   105, 108, 104, 101, 109

**2**   Lily recorded the heights in cm of a group of her friends.

    Girls      144     149     142     140     150

    Boys      143     148     141

    **a**   Calculate the mean height for the boys.

    **b**   Calculate the mean height for the girls.

    **c**   Calculate the mean height for the whole group.

**3**   Gemma records the pocket money received per week by each
of her five friends. These are her results given in pounds.

    2    5    3    5    40

    **a**   Find the mean amount of pocket money received.

    **b**   Is this a fair indication of the average amount of pocket
money received? Explain your answer.

    **c**   Is there another average that may be more appropriate
for Gemma to use? Calculate this average.

**MyMaths**.co.uk

A drinks machine sells tea, coffee and cocoa and the bar chart shows the sales for a certain day.
Find what fraction of the drinks were

**a** tea      **b** coffee      **c** cocoa.

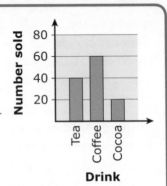

**Drink**

Total number of drinks
sold = 40 + 60 + 20 = 120

**a** Tea = $\frac{40}{120} = \frac{1}{3}$

**b** Coffee = $\frac{60}{120} = \frac{1}{2}$

**c** Cocoa = $\frac{20}{120} = \frac{1}{6}$

**1** Are these statements true or false?
Explain your answers.

**Transport to school**

**a** Half the students in each class walk to school.

**b** The same number of students in classes 2A and 2B walk to school.

**c** Less than a quarter of the students in class 2A cycle to school.

**Class 2A**

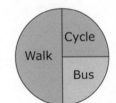
**Class 2B**

**2** Leah displayed the number of siblings of each student in her class.

**a** Write the modal number of siblings.

**b** How many students are there in Leah's class?

**c** Write the fraction of students that have   **i** 0   **ii** 1   **iii** 2 sibling(s).

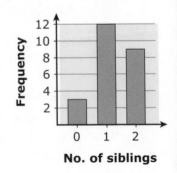

**No. of siblings**

**MyMaths**.co.uk

Q 1205, 1206   **SEARCH**

Eleanor wants to investigate how people make their choice
when deciding to buy a new car. Suggest some specific questions
that Eleanor could ask.

How often do people change their car?
Do people buy second-hand or brand new cars?
Are people influenced by the popularity of the make of car?

1   David wants to investigate how people choose which
    washing powder to buy. Suggest three specific questions
    that David could ask.

2   Dr Graddon needed to know how his students view
    their Mathematics lessons. Suggest three specific questions
    that he could investigate.

3   Val needs to buy a selection of new books for the school library.
    She decides to investigate these questions.
    a   Do students use the library for reading for pleasure or
        helping with school work?
    b   Which is the school subject that students most use the
        school library for help with?
    c   Which are the most popular children's books?

    Suggest some possible sources of data that Val could use to
    help her answer these questions.

**MyMaths**.co.uk

# 8h  Collecting data

**Example**

Jasminda wants to find out how much pocket money each of the students in her class receives each week. She asks every student this question.

'How much pocket money do you receive each week?'

The answers she gets are rather vague. How could she improve her question?

Jasminda's question was very 'open-ended'. Her answers would have been much better if she had given every student a piece of paper like the one shown and asked them to tick the appropriate box.

| | |
|---|---|
| Less than £1 | ☐ |
| £1 to £5 | ☐ |
| £5 to £10 | ☐ |
| More than £10 | ☐ |

1 These survey questions are not very good.
   How could you improve each question?
   a  Where do you like to go for your holidays?
   b  How long do you spend per evening on your homework?
   c  What kind of TV programmes do you like?
   d  What kind of music do you like listening to?
   e  What is your address?

2 Davina asks this question in a survey about healthy eating.
   Explain the problem with the choices and write an improved version.
   How many times a week do you eat a packet of crisps?
   ☐ I don't eat crisps      ☐ 1–3
   ☐ 3–5                     ☐ more than 5

3 Candace wants to find out whether or not students think their teachers set them too much homework. She waits at the school gate and asks the first twenty students that she sees. Is this a good sample?
   How could she improve her investigation?

MyMaths.co.uk

1249  SEARCH

**Example**

A school football team played in 15 matches.
The number of goals they scored were:
1, 2, 0, 1, 1, 3, 2, 4, 0, 4, 1, 2, 4, 3 and 0.
Draw a tally chart and display the data on a bar chart.

| Number of goals | Tally | Frequency |
|---|---|---|
| 0 | \|\|\| | 3 |
| 1 | \|\|\|\| | 4 |
| 2 | \|\|\| | 3 |
| 3 | \|\| | 2 |
| 4 | \|\|\| | 3 |

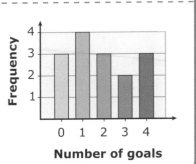

**1** These are the marks that the pupils in class 7C obtained
in a Science test.

3    6    5    7    1    8    6    7    8    4

7    8    3    0    9    7    2    3    5    6

5    9    7    8    10   4    1    6    7    6

**a** Draw a tally chart for these marks.

**b** Use your tally chart to draw a frequency table for this data.

**c** Show the data from your frequency table as a bar chart.

**2** These are the numbers of cartons of milk that the milkman delivered
to the houses in Park Close.

3    1    3    2    4    2    1

2    4    3    5    2    1    6

4    5    2    3    1    2

**a** Draw a tally chart to find the frequencies for the
numbers of cartons of milk delivered.

**b** Draw a frequency table for this data.

**c** Draw a bar chart for this data.

The numbers of newspapers that two newsagents sold in one week from Monday to Saturday were:

First shop 80, 70, 60, 80, 90 and 100
Second shop 90, 70, 80, 80, 90 and 100

Compare the sales of newspapers in the two shops. Use the mean and range.

For the first shop the range is $100 - 60 = 40$

and the mean is $\frac{(80 + 70 + 60 + 80 + 90 + 100)}{6} = \frac{480}{6} = 80$

For the second shop the range is $100 - 70 = 30$

and the mean is $\frac{(90 + 70 + 80 + 80 + 90 + 100)}{6} = \frac{510}{6} = 85$

The second shop has a smaller range so there was less variety each day, but a higher mean so it sold more papers on average.

1 Twins, Imogen and Olivia, each believe that they have achieved the best end of year examination results. These are their percentages.

| | Maths | English | Science | French | History |
|---|---|---|---|---|---|
| **Imogen** | 84 | 73 | 78 | 93 | 62 |
| **Olivia** | 82 | 78 | 80 | 83 | 67 |

a Calculate **i** the mean **ii** the range for each set of results.
b Compare the twins' results using your calculations from part **a**.

2 The twins' French teacher looks at the marks in French Paper 1 and French Paper 2 for the whole class. These are her calculations, given as percentages.

| French paper | Median | Range |
|---|---|---|
| 1 | 65 | 40 |
| 2 | 75 | 25 |

Compare the data for French Paper 1 and French Paper 2.

**MyMaths**.co.uk

Q 1192    **SEARCH**

Draw the reflection of this shape using the mirror line.

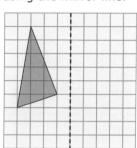

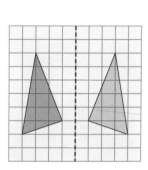

**1** Copy each diagram. Draw and label the mirror line.

**a**

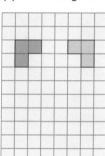

**b**

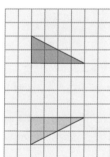

**c**

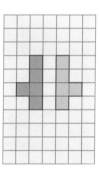

**2** Copy each diagram and reflect each shape in the mirror line.

**a**

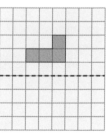

**b**

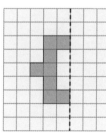

**c**

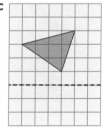

Copy the shape and draw the lines of symmetry.

There are four lines of symmetry.

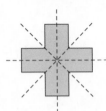

**1 a** Copy each of these quadrilaterals and draw the lines of symmetry if possible.

i 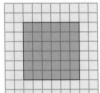 ii  iii 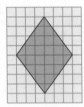 iv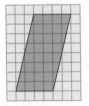

**b** Write the name of each quadrilateral in part **a**.

**2 a** Draw and name a quadrilateral with only one line of symmetry.

**b** Is it possible to draw a quadrilateral with more than four lines of symmetry?

**3** Copy these road signs and draw the lines of symmetry, if possible.

**a**

**b**

**c**

**d**

# 9c Rotation

Copy the diagram and rotate the shape through 90° clockwise about the point.

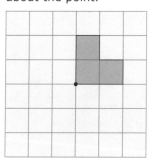 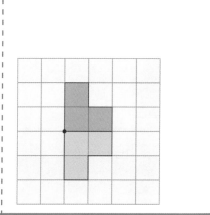

1  For each of these rotations write
   i   the angle of rotation
   ii  the direction of rotation.
   The centre of rotation is shown as a dot.

   **a**                **b**                **c**                **d**

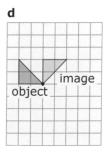

2  Copy and rotate each shape through the given angle using the dot as the centre of rotation.

   **a**                **b**                **c**                **d**

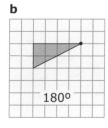 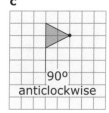 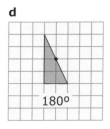

90° clockwise        180°        90° anticlockwise        180°

## MyMaths.co.uk

**Example**

What is the order of rotation symmetry for this shape?

The shape looks exactly like itself four times in a complete turn. The shape has rotation symmetry of order 4.

**1** Copy each shape and state its order of rotation symmetry.

a

b

c

d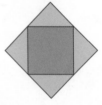

e

f

**2** Three upper case letters (other than O) have rotation symmetry, but no lines of symmetry. Which three letters are these and what is the order of rotation symmetry for each?

**3** Two digits (other than zero) have rotation symmetry. Which two digits are these and what is the order of rotation symmetry for each?

MyMaths.co.uk

Q 1116 SEARCH

**a** Draw a triangle with vertices $(0,0)$, $(1,2)$, $(1,0)$.

**b** Translate the triangle by two units to the right and three units up.

**c** Write the coordinates of the vertices of the image.

**a b**

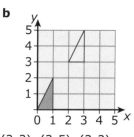

**c** $(2,3)$, $(3,5)$, $(3,3)$

**1 a** Copy this rectangle on to square grid paper. Label the rectangle A.

**b** Draw the image of this rectangle after a translation of 6 units to the right and three units up. Label this rectangle B.

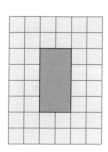

**2** Describe the translation of these triangles.

| | | | |
|---|---|---|---|
| **a** | A to B | **b** | A to C |
| **c** | B to C | **d** | B to D |
| **e** | C to D | **f** | C to E |
| **g** | D to E | **h** | E to A |

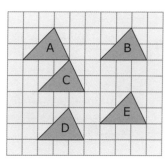

**3** On square grid paper draw a set of coordinate axes from 0 to 10.

**a** Draw the kite with vertices $(2,0)$, $(1,2)$, $(2,3)$ and $(3,2)$. Label this kite A.

**b** Translate kite A by two units to the right and five units up. Label the image B.

**c** Translate kite B by 4 units to the right. Label the image C.

**d** Describe the translation that would take kite A directly to kite C.

Tessellate this rhombus.

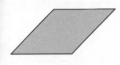

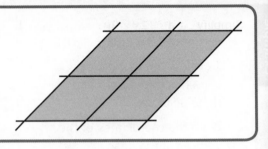

**1** Name these shapes and show how each one tessellates.

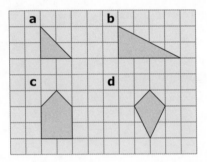

**2** Copy these tessellations and add 6 more tiles to continue each pattern.

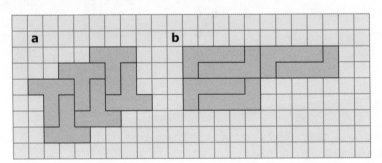

Simplify    **a**   $12x \times 9y$             **b**  $150z \div 50$

---

**a**   $12x \times 9y = 108xy$     **b**  $150z \div 50 = 3z$

**1**   Simplify these expressions.

**a**   $5 \times 4x$           **b**   $8 \times 3z$           **c**   $6 \times 9u$
**d**   $8m \times 4$           **e**   $7p \times 6$           **f**   $15a \times 4$

**2**   Find the perimeters of these regular shapes.

**a**
$5x$

**b**
$20z$

**c**
$16u$

**3**   Simplify these expressions.

**a**   $5x \times 2y$           **b**   $12u \times 7v$           **c**   $25p \times 6q$
**d**   $3x \times 20y$           **e**   $5u \times 14v$           **f**   $4p \times 18q$

**4**   Simplify these expressions.

**a**   $8x \div 2$             **b**   $12k \div 3$
**c**   $30x \div 5$             **d**   $45y \div 9$
**e**   $\dfrac{60\,m}{12}$       **f**   $\dfrac{100\,v}{4}$
**g**   $\dfrac{80t}{16}$         **h**   $\dfrac{120\,p}{8}$

**5**   Find the missing side length for this rectangle.

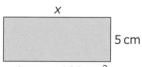
$x$
$5\,cm$
Area $= 100\,cm^2$

Calculate the weight of the
parcel marked with ?.

$9 + ? = 10 + 15$
$9 + ? = 25$
$? = 25 - 9$
$? = 16$

**1** Copy these calculations and decide whether
each one balances. Use ✓ or ✗.

**a** $30 - 5 = 5 \times 5$      **b** $17 + 3 = 26 - 6$

**c** $4 \times 7 = 18 + 9$      **d** $24 \div 2 = 6 \times 2$

**e** $9 + 8 + 7 = 50 - 25$      **f** $3 \times 14 = 13 + 14 + 15$

**2** All of these scales are balanced.
Calculate the weight of each parcel marked with ?.

**a**

**b**

**c**

**d**

**e**

**f**

**3** Calculate the value of the ? in each question.

**a** $? + 4 = 15$      **b** $? - 9 = 12$

**c** $? + 14 = 20 + 5$      **d** $5 + 19 = ? + 8$

**e** $? + 11 = 20 - 6$      **f** $? + 19 = 9 + 10$

**MyMaths**.co.uk

Q 1154   SEARCH

# 10c Simple equations

Solve this equation.

$$a - 37 = 53$$

- - - - - - - - - - - - - - - - - - - - - - - - - - - - - - - - - - - - - - - - - - - -

$$a - 37 = 53$$
$$a - 37 + 37 = 53 + 37 \quad \text{Add 37 to both sides.}$$
$$a = 90$$

**1** Write these balance drawings as equations.

**a**

**b**

**c**

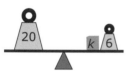

**d** Solve each equation to calculate the weight of each box marked with a letter. Use balancing operations.

**2** Solve these equations. Show your balancing operations.

| | | |
|---|---|---|
| **a** $x + 5 = 9$ | **b** $a + 3 = 11$ | **c** $t + 10 = 21$ |
| **d** $p + 6 = 30$ | **e** $g - 12 = 13$ | **f** $h - 15 = 1$ |
| **g** $k - 9 = 25$ | **h** $15 + b = 28$ | **i** $45 + m = 59$ |
| **j** $d - 100 = 100$ | **k** $35 = n + 19$ | **l** $27 = q - 15$ |

**3** Josiah is travelling from Carlisle to Newcastle, a distance of 100 km. When he gets to Hexham, how much further does he have to go? Solve this equation to find the answer.

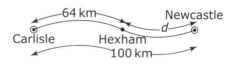

$$64 + d = 100$$

**4** Rapinda is travelling from Manchester to Hull, a distance of 161 km. When she gets to Sheffield she knows she has 96 km of her journey left. Write and solve an equation to find $d$, the distance from Manchester to Sheffield.

Solve these equations.   **a**   $9y = 27$      **b**   $\frac{x}{4} = 5$

**a**     $9y = 27$                    **b**   $\frac{x}{4} = 5$

     $9y \div 9 = 27 \div 9$              $\frac{x}{4} \times 4 = 5 \times 4$

         $y = 3$                         $x = 20$

**1  a**  Write these balance drawings as equations.

**i**    **ii**    **iii**

  **b**  Solve each equation in part **a** to calculate the weight of each
box marked with a letter. Use balancing operations.

**2**  Solve these equations. Show your balancing operations.

    **a**  $2x = 6$          **b**  $4a = 12$          **c**  $3p = 18$

    **d**  $8m = 24$        **e**  $6c = 48$          **f**  $9b = 54$

    **g**  $60 = 20q$     **h**  $7d = 0$           **i**  $10f = 10$

    **j**  $56 = 8g$       **k**  $45 = 15k$       **l**  $4t = 2$

**3**  Solve these equations by multiplying both sides by the
same amount.

    **a**  $\frac{x}{2} = 3$          **b**  $\frac{a}{5} = 2$          **c**  $\frac{p}{4} = 5$

    **d**  $6 = \frac{m}{9}$        **e**  $7 = \frac{c}{10}$        **f**  $\frac{b}{3} = 12$

    **g**  $\frac{q}{5} = 20$       **h**  $\frac{d}{8} = 8$        **i**  $30 = \frac{f}{7}$

    **j**  $\frac{g}{6} = 1$         **k**  $5 = \frac{k}{100}$     **l**  $\frac{t}{25} = 0$

Solve for $x$      **a**   $2x - 5 = 7$      **b**   $\dfrac{x}{2} + 3 = 7$

- - - - - - - - - - - - - - - - - - - - - - - - - - - - - - - - - - - - -

**a**    $2x - 5 = 7$

     $2x - 5 + 5 = 7 + 5$

           $2x = 12$

      $2x \div 2 = 12 \div 2$

            $x = 6$

**b**    $\dfrac{x}{2} + 3 = 7$

    $\dfrac{x}{2} + 3 - 3 = 7 - 3$

           $\dfrac{x}{2} = 4$

     $\dfrac{x}{2} \times 2 = 4 \times 2$

           $x = 8$

**1**   **a**   Write an equation to represent each balance drawing.

**i** 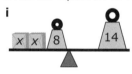   **ii** 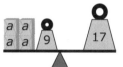   **iii**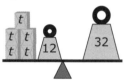

   **b**   Solve each equation in part **a** to calculate the weight of each box marked with a letter.

**2**   Use two balancing operations to solve each equation.

   **a**   $2x + 9 = 19$      **b**   $3b + 6 = 18$      **c**   $5k - 10 = 5$

   **d**   $8m + 2 = 26$     **e**   $6p - 5 = 7$       **f**   $11 + 4t = 25$

   **g**   $20 + 7a = 41$    **h**   $12n - 7 = 29$     **i**   $15 = 6x + 9$

   **j**   $79 = 10p + 9$    **k**   $4q + 5 = 15$       **l**   $5 = 5 + 9d$

**3**   Use two balancing operations to solve each equation.

   **a**   $\dfrac{x}{2} + 4 = 9$      **b**   $\dfrac{a}{3} + 8 = 10$      **c**   $\dfrac{k}{6} + 4 = 7$

   **d**   $\dfrac{t}{3} - 5 = 2$      **e**   $\dfrac{p}{4} - 1 = 4$      **f**   $9 + \dfrac{b}{5} = 14$

   **g**   $11 + \dfrac{d}{8} = 13$    **h**   $\dfrac{m}{7} - 4 = 1$      **i**   $15 = \dfrac{n}{2} + 3$

   **j**   $10 = \dfrac{x}{9} + 6$     **k**   $\dfrac{1}{3}p - 3 = 9$      **l**   $7 = 7 + \dfrac{1}{10}t$

**4**   Marcus weighs $w$ kg. His father weighs 3 times as much and his younger brother Jack weighs only 20 kg. If his father and Jack both stand on a weighing machine together the reading is 110 kg. Find the value of $w$.

List the factors of 16.

- - - - - - - - - - - - - - - - - - - - - - - - - - - - - - - - - - - - - - - -

**16** = 1 × 16, 2 × 8 or 4 × 4
So the factors of 16 are 1, 2, 4, 8 and 16.

**1** List the first five multiples of these numbers.
   **a** 2     **b** 5     **c** 6     **d** 9     **e** 12

**2** List all the factors of these numbers.
   **a** 3     **b** 4     **c** 10     **d** 18     **e** 25

**3** True or false? Explain each answer.
   **a** 38 is an even number.
   **b** 85 is a multiple of 5.
   **c** 4 is a factor of 34.
   **d** 72 will divide by 3 exactly.

**4** Gemma wins £68.43 on the lottery.
   She decides to give an equal share to each of her three children.
   Can this be done?

**5** Clare makes 114 cards to sell at a Christmas fair.
   If Clare bundles her cards into packs of 4,
   will she have an exact number of packs?

**6** True or false?
   Any multiple of 6 is also a multiple of 2 and a multiple of 3.

Calculate $19^2$

Using a calculator:  `1` `9` $x^2$ `=` | 361

1 Without using a calculator, write the values of these.
   a  $3^2 = 3 \times \square = \square$      b  $5^2 = 5 \times \square = \square$
   c  $8^2 = \square \times \square = \square$      d  $9^2 = \square \times \square = \square$
   e  $10^2 = \square \times \square = \square$      f  $12^2 = \square \times \square = \square$

2 Use your calculator to find the values of these
   square numbers.
   a  $13^2$      b  $17^2$      c  $31^2$      d  $35^2$      e  $70^2$

3 a  Copy and continue this sequence for three more lines.
         $1 = 1$
       $1 + 3 = 4$
     $1 + 3 + 5 = 9$

   b  What type of numbers are on the left-hand side of
      each equation in part a?
   c  What type of numbers are on the right-hand side of
      each equation in part a?

4 Work out the areas of these.

   a   55 cm
   [square]   55 cm

   Candace's
   chess board

   b   85 m
   [square]   85 m

   The playground at
   Tom's school

   c   72 m
   [square]   72 m

   A swimming pool in
   a pleasure park

Work out the length of the side of this square.

25 cm²

---

$5 \times 5 = 25$ so $\sqrt{25} = 5$    The side length is 5 cm.

**1**  Without using a calculator, calculate the square roots of these.
    **a**  4       **b**  9       **c**  36    **d**  49    **e**  100

**2**  Calculate the square roots of these.
    **a**  324    **b**  1296   **c**  225   **d**  2025   **e**  6400

**3**  Find the side lengths of these.

    **a**

Area
22 500 mm²

A table
mat

    **b**

Area
62 500 m²

A playing field at
Shani's school

    **c**

Area
40 000 km²

The Wollabongbong
National Park in Australia

**4**  The square roots of these numbers are not whole numbers.
    Say which two whole numbers the square root lies between.
    **a**  20    **b**  75    **c**  55    **d**  12    **e**  3

**a** Write all the different multiplications of two numbers that give an answer of 60.
**b** Use part **a** to write all the factors of 60.

- - - - - - - - - - - - - - - - - - - - - - - - - - - - - - - - - - - - - - - -

**a** 1 × 60, 2 × 30, 3 × 20, 4 × 15, 5 × 12, 6 × 10
**b** The factors of 60 are all the different numbers that appear in the list in part **a**. These are 1, 2, 3, 4, 5, 6, 10, 12, 15, 20, 30, 60.

**1** Write the first five multiples of
  **a** 3    **b** 5    **c** 6    **d** 10    **e** 50

**2** Write all the factors of
  **a** 2    **b** 7    **c** 9    **d** 10    **e** 18

**3**  ( 3   4   5   9   10 )
  From this box of numbers write
  **a** two multiples of 5        **b** two factors of 9
  **c** two prime numbers        **d** two square numbers.

**4** Use divisibility tests for 2, 3 and 5 to match each number in the box with one description.

  ( 396    450    585    710 )
  **a** It divides by 2 and 3 but not by 5.
  **b** It divides by 2 and 5 but not by 3.
  **c** It divides by 3 and 5 but not by 2.
  **d** It divides by 2, 3 and 5.

**5** Use divisibility tests to decide which of these are prime.
  **a** 95    **b** 61    **c** 81    **d** 78    **e** 97

**6** Find the factors of these and state how many factors each one has.
  **a** 25    **b** 81    **c** 9    **d** 16    **e** 36
  What do you notice about the numbers and the number of factors they have?

⊞ **MyMaths**.co.uk

**a** Find the HCF of 16 and 24.    **b** Find the LCM of 10 and 12.

**a** Factors of 16 are: 1, 2, 4, ⑧, 16
Factors of 24 are: 1, 2, 3, 4, 6, ⑧, 12, 24
The HCF is 8.

**b** Multiples of 10 are: 10, 20, 30, 40, 50, ⑥⓪
Multiples of 12 are: 12, 24, 36, 48, ⑥⓪, 72
The LCM is 60.

**1** **a** List the first five multiples of 2.
  **b** List the first five multiples of 5.
  **c** Use your lists to write the LCM of 2 and 5.

**2** Find the LCM of
  **a** 3 and 5    **b** 6 and 10
  **c** 12 and 15    **d** 18 and 24

**3** **a** List the factors of 6.
  **b** List the factors of 15.
  **c** Use your lists to write the HCF of 6 and 15.

**4** Find the HCF of
  **a** 9 and 21    **b** 12 and 18
  **c** 15 and 24    **d** 32 and 40

**5** Write each of these fractions in their simplest form.

  **a** $\frac{16}{18}$  **b** $\frac{25}{30}$  **c** $\frac{4}{48}$  **d** $\frac{12}{80}$  **e** $\frac{72}{108}$

**6** Write the numbers as a fraction of the total, and write
each fraction to its lowest terms.
  **a** One day a trainspotter sees 120 trains. 72 of them are
  passenger trains and 48 of them are freight trains.
  **b** One day when Jane is waiting for a bus she sees 150 vehicles pass.
  75 of them are cars, 45 of them are vans and 30 are lorries.

**⊕ MyMaths**.co.uk
Q 1034, 1044  SEARCH

Make an accurate copy of this diagram.

Extend the unmarked sides to a point C
to make a triangle. Measure the angle
at C and the lengths of the sides AC and BC.

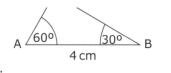

The angle at C = 90°,
AC = 2 cm and BC = 3.5 cm.

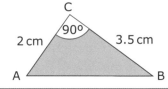

**1** Construct these triangles. State the type of triangle for each question.

**a**

**b**

**c**

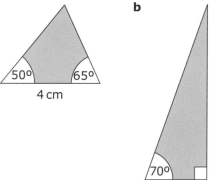

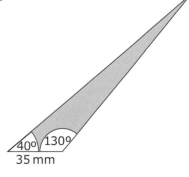

**2** Make an accurate copy of each diagram. Extend the unmarked sides to
a point C to make a triangle. Measure and write the angle at C and give
the length of each of the sides AC and BC.

**a**

**b**

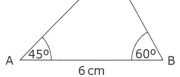

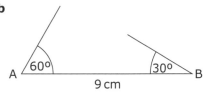

Construct a triangle with the angle at A equal to 90° and both AB and AC equal to 3.5cm. Measure the size of the angles at B and C and name this triangle.

The angles at B and C are both equal to 45° and the triangle is isosceles.

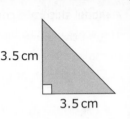
3.5 cm
3.5 cm

**1** Construct these triangles (SAS).
State the type of triangle for each question.

**a**
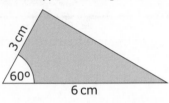
3 cm
60°
6 cm

**b**
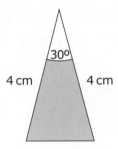
30°
4 cm    4 cm

**2** Construct these triangles (ASA).
State the type of triangle for each question.

**a**
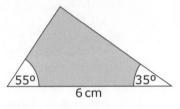
55°
6 cm
35°

**b**
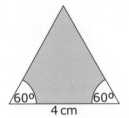
60°    60°
4 cm

**3** Construct these triangles.
   **a** Triangle ABC: A = 50°, AB = 4.5cm and AC = 3.5cm
   **b** Triangle PQR: PQ = 5.5cm, P = 25° and Q = 65°

**4** Construct this quadrilateral.
Name the shape that you have drawn.

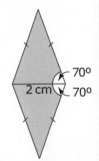
70°
2 cm
70°

⊞ **MyMaths**.co.uk

Q 1090    SEARCH

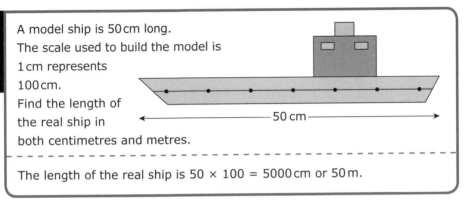

A model ship is 50 cm long.
The scale used to build the model is
1 cm represents
100 cm.
Find the length of
the real ship in
both centimetres and metres.

50 cm

------------------------------------------------

The length of the real ship is 50 × 100 = 5000 cm or 50 m.

**1** A door on the plan of a house measures 2.5 cm by 1 cm.
The scale of the plan is 1 cm represents 80 cm.
Find the real-life dimensions of the door.

2.5 cm

1 cm

**2** On a plan, a garden measures 3 cm by 2 cm.

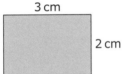

3 cm

2 cm

The scale of the plan is 1 cm represents 1000 cm.
Find the dimensions of the real garden.
Give your answers in both centimetres and metres.

**3** A doll's house is a scale model of a real house.
The scale is 1 cm represents 15 cm.
If the doll's house is 100 cm long, 80 cm wide and
60 cm high, find the dimensions of the real house.
Give your answers in both centimetres and metres.

**4** Measure the length of Green Park
Road on the map.
If the scale of the map is 1 cm represents
2000 cm, find the real length of Green Park
Road in both centimetres and metres.

Green Park Road

This is a pentagonal prism.
State the number of

**a** faces **b** vertices **c** edges.

- - - - - - - - - - - - - - - - - - - - - - - - - - - - - - - - - - - -

**a** 7 faces **b** 10 vertices **c** 15 edges

**1 a** Copy and complete this table about pyramids.

| Picture | Name | Number of faces | Number of vertices | Number of edges |
|---------|------|-----------------|--------------------|-----------------|
| | | 4 | | |
| | | | 5 | |
| | Hexagonal-based pyramid | | | 12 |

**b** Describe the relationship between the number of faces and the number of vertices of a pyramid.

**2 a** Copy and complete this table about prisms.

| Picture | Name | Number of faces | Number of vertices | Number of edges |
|---------|------|-----------------|--------------------|-----------------|
| | | 5 | | |
| | | | 8 | |
| | Hexagonal-based prism | | | 18 |

**b** Copy and complete this sentence.

'To find the number of vertices of a prism, multiply the number of faces by 2 and ☐☐ .'

**3** For each solid in questions **1** and **2** work out the number of faces + number of vertices − number of edges. Describe what you notice.

Two cubes are added to this solid in order to make a cuboid. Draw the cuboid and state its dimensions.

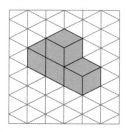

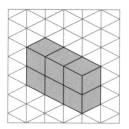

The cuboid measures 3 units by 1 unit by 2 units.

**1** Draw these cuboids on isometric paper.

**a**

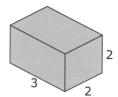

2

3

2

**b**

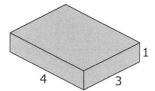

1

4

3

**2** Four cubes are added to each of these solids in order to make cuboids. Draw each cuboid on isometric paper and state its dimensions.

**a**

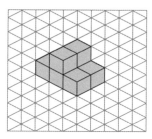

**b**

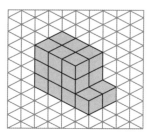

**3 a** Draw a 3 cm by 1 cm by 3 cm cuboid on isometric paper.

   **b** Draw the cuboid after the four corner cubes are removed.

Here is a net of a cuboid.
Write down the dimensions of the
cuboid and find its surface area.

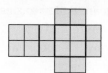

- - - - - - - - - - - - - - - - - - - - - - - - - - - - - - - - - - - - - - -

The dimensions of the cuboid are 2 cm, 2 cm and 1 cm.
Its surface area is
2 × (2 × 2) + 4 × (2 × 1) = 8 + 8 = 16 square centimetres.

**1** These nets each make a cuboid. Write the dimensions
and find the surface area of each cuboid.

**a**

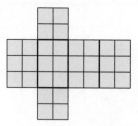

**b**

**2** For each cuboid write the dimensions, draw a net
and find the surface area.

**a**

**b**

**3** Draw a net of each solid.

**a**

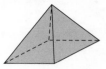

**b**

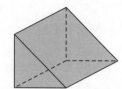

MyMaths.co.uk

Q 1106   SEARCH

Find the volume of this cuboid.

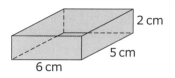

2 cm
5 cm
6 cm

Volume = length × width × height
= 6 × 5 × 2 = 60 cubic centimetres

**1** Calculate the volume of these solids made from centimetre cubes.

a 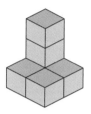    b 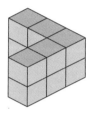    c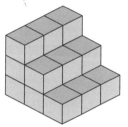

**2** Find the volume of these shapes which are made from
1 centimetre cubes.

a 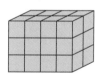    b 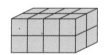    c

**3** If each dice is a 1 centimetre cube,
how many dice will fit into the dice box?
Use your answer to find the volume
of the box.

2 cm
DICE
3 cm
4 cm

**4** 20 cubes are arranged to form a cuboid. Write the dimensions of
the four possible cuboids that can be made.

Write **a** the sequence for the number of squares
in this pattern

**b** the next four terms
of the sequence.

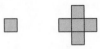 

- - - - - - - - - - - - - - - - - - - - - - - - - - - - - - - - - - - -

**a** The sequence is 1, 5, 9.

**b** The numbers start at 1 and increase by 4.
The next four terms are 13, 17, 21, 25.

**1** This pattern of squares is made by joining the dots.

    **a** Copy and complete this table.

| Number of squares | 1 | 2 | 3 | 4 |
|---|---|---|---|---|
| Number of dots | 4 | 6 | | |

    **b** Write out the sequence for the number of dots.

    **c** Extend this sequence by another four terms.

**2 a** Using the pattern of squares in question **1**, copy and complete this
new table.

| Number of squares | 1 | 2 | 3 | 4 |
|---|---|---|---|---|
| Number of lines | 4 | 7 | | |

    **b** Write out the sequence for the number of lines.

    **c** Extend this sequence by another four terms.

**3** This is a pattern of squares.

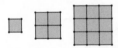

    **a** Write the sequence of the pattern as it grows.

    **b** Extend your sequence by another four terms.

MyMaths.co.uk

Q 1173   SEARCH

**a** Write the rule for this sequence ☐, ☐, ☐, 18, 23, 28
**b** Find the missing values.

**a** 18    23    28          The rule is +5
     +5    +5
**b** To find the term before 18 *subtract* 5.   18 − 5 = 13
The sequence is    ③, ⑧, ⑬, 18, 23, 28

**1** Look at this number pattern.

$$3 \times 7 = 21$$
$$33 \times 7 = 231$$
$$333 \times 7 = 2331$$
$$3333 \times 7 = 23331$$

Write the next two lines in this pattern.

**2** **a** Copy each sequence.
     **b** Add three more terms to each sequence.
     **c** Write the rule for each sequence.

        **i**   5, 8, 11, __, __, __      **ii**   36, 29, 22, __, __, __
        **iii**   3, 12, 48, __, __, __      **iv**   243, 81, 27, __, __, __

**3** Find the first five terms for each sequence.

| | **First term** | **Rule** |
|---|---|---|
| **a** | 4 | + 7 |
| **b** | 2 | × 5 |
| **c** | 29 | − 4 |
| **d** | 1024 | ÷ 2 |

**4** Find the first three terms for each sequence.

     **a**   __, __, __, 15, 19, 23      **b**   __, __, __, 19, 11, 3
     **c**   __, __, __, 40, 80, 160      **d**   __, __, __, 75, 15, 3

Write the rule for this sequence and give the next three terms.
9, 4, −1, —, —, —

The rule is start at 9 and subtract 5. The next three terms are
−6, −11, −16.

1   A sequence has first term = 4.
    The term-to-term rule is 'add 3'.
    Write the first five terms of this sequence.

2   Generate the first five terms of the sequence whose first term
    is 10 and term-to-term rule is 'subtract 2'.

3   The term-to-term rule for this sequence is 'multiply by 3'.
    ☐, ☐, ☐, 27, 81, 243, . . .
    Find the missing terms.

4   For each of these sequences
    i   Extend the sequence to the 6th term.
    ii  Write the term-to-term rule for the sequence.
    a   5, 13, 21, 29, . . .          b   45, 39, 33, 27, . . .
    c   2, 4, 8, 16, . . .            d   27, 21, 15, 9, . . .
    e   112, 56, 28, 14, . . .        f   1, $1\frac{1}{2}$, 2, $2\frac{1}{2}$, . . .
    g   2, 6, 18, 54, . . .           h   5.0, 4.8, 4.6, 4.4, . . .

**MyMaths**.co.uk
Q 1173      SEARCH

Look at this pattern made with straws.

1st position     2nd position     3rd position
(4 straws)       (7 straws)       (10 straws)

Copy and complete the position-to-term rule:
'The total number of straws is ☐ times the position number then add ☐.'

- - - - - - - - - - - - - - - - - - - - - - - - - - - - - - - - - - - - - - - - -

The term-to-term rule is 'add 3' so the position-to-term rule will be:
'The total number of straws is **3** times the position number then add ☐.'
Compare the sequence with the three times-table
4, 7, 10
3, 6, 9
So the rule is
'The total number of straws is **3** times the position number then add **1**.'

**1** Look at this pattern made with tiles.

   **a** Draw the pattern of tiles in position 4.
   **b** Copy and complete the position-to-term rule:
      'The total number of tiles is ☐ times the
      position number then add ☐.'
   **c** Find the number of tiles in position
      **i** 5         **ii** 10

**2** Look at this pattern made with straws.

   **a** Draw the pattern of straws in position 4.
   **b** Copy and complete this table.

| Position number | 1 | 2 | 3 | 4 |
|---|---|---|---|---|
| Number of straws | 5 | 9 | | |

   **c** Copy and complete the position-to-term rule:
      'The number of straws is ☐ times the position number then add ☐.'
   **d** Use the position-to-term rule to find the number of tiles in position
      **i** 5         **ii** 10

Calculate

**a** 750 ÷ 6 using the method of partitioning

**b** 1.2 × 30 using the method of factors.

- - - - - - - - - - - - - - - - - - - - - - - - - - - - - - - - - -

**a** 750 ÷ 6 = (600 ÷ 6) + (150 ÷ 6)

$\qquad$ = 100 + 25

$\qquad$ = 125

**b** 1.2 × 30 = 1.2 × 10 × 3

$\qquad$ = 12 × 3

$\qquad$ = 36

**1** Calculate these using the method of factors.

$\quad$ **a** 7 × 80 $\qquad$ **b** 5 × 600 $\qquad$ **c** 5.3 × 20 $\qquad$ **d** 4.1 × 300

**2** Calculate these using the method of factors.

$\quad$ **a** 300 ÷ 4 $\qquad$ **b** 960 ÷ 5 $\qquad$ **c** 174 ÷ 6 $\qquad$ **d** 256 ÷ 8

**3** Calculate these using the method of partitioning.

$\quad$ **a** 5 × 17 $\qquad$ **b** 12 × 15 $\qquad$ **c** 6.4 × 11 $\qquad$ **d** 12 × 2.4

**4** Calculate these using the method of partitioning.

$\quad$ **a** 344 ÷ 8 $\qquad$ **b** 294 ÷ 7 $\qquad$ **c** 636 ÷ 4 $\qquad$ **d** 945 ÷ 15

**5** Calculate these using the method of doubling and halving.

$\quad$ **a** 2.5 × 24 $\qquad$ **b** 5.5 × 16 $\qquad$ **c** 4.5 × 18 $\qquad$ **d** 8 × 10.5

**6** Use an appropriate method to solve each of these problems.

$\quad$ **a** Barbara needs pieces of curtain wire, each of length 2.2 m, for 8 windows. What total length of wire does she need to buy?

$\quad$ **b** Malcolm pours out 21 glasses of champagne. Each glass has a capacity of 0.25 litres. How many litres of champagne does Malcolm use?

**MyMaths**.co.uk

Q 1010, 1382 | SEARCH

**Example**

Calculate 8 × 38.3

A rough estimate is 8 × 40 = 320.
You can multiply 8 × 383 and then ÷ 10

| ×  | 300  | 80  | 3  |
|----|------|-----|----|
| 8  | 2400 | 640 | 24 |

2400 + 640 + 24 = 3064
3064 ÷ 10 = 306.4

**1** **a** Copy and complete this estimate.
134 × 18 ≈ 100 × ☐ = ☐
**b** Copy and complete this grid to calculate 134 × 18.

| ×  | 100              | 30 | 4 |
|----|------------------|----|---|
| 10 | 100 × 10 = 1000  |    |   |
| 8  |                  |    |   |

**2** Calculate these using an appropriate method.
**a** 8 × 32 **b** 9 × 58 **c** 7 × 93 **d** 3 × 416
**e** 5 × 947 **f** 6 × 833 **g** 14 × 248 **h** 25 × 193

**3** Calculate these using an appropriate method.
**a** 6 × 4.8 **b** 4 × 3.7 **c** 8 × 5.9 **d** 3 × 3.25
**e** 6 × 8.06 **f** 8 × 45.5 **g** 13 × 5.83 **h** 24 × 18.1

**4** **a** A CD costs £9.77. Work out the cost of 5 CDs.
**b** Diesel costs 97.5p per litre. Work out the cost of 8 litres in pounds.

**5** The distance from London to Peterborough is 121.6 km.
A train driver has to complete this journey 4 times each day.
What is the total distance per day that he drives his train?

**Example**

Calculate    45 ÷ 6

$6\overline{)45}$
$\underline{-42}$  ⟵  6 × ⑦ = 42
3
$\underline{-3}$  ⟵  6 × ⓪.5 = 3
0

So, 45 ÷ 6 = 7.5

**1** Calculate these using an appropriate method.
The whole number answers can all be found
in the box.

( 21  26  29  37  46  48  51  52 )

| | | | |
|---|---|---|---|
| **a** 255 ÷ 5 | **b** 312 ÷ 6 | **c** 368 ÷ 8 | **d** 336 ÷ 7 |
| **e** 273 ÷ 13 | **f** 407 ÷ 11 | **g** 442 ÷ 17 | **h** 551 ÷ 19 |

**2** Calculate these giving your answer as a number
and a remainder.

| | | | |
|---|---|---|---|
| **a** 102 ÷ 8 | **b** 157 ÷ 4 | **c** 265 ÷ 8 | **d** 572 ÷ 5 |
| **e** 214 ÷ 15 | **f** 363 ÷ 17 | **g** 499 ÷ 14 | **h** 759 ÷ 16 |

**3** Calculate these giving your answer as a
decimal number.

| | | | |
|---|---|---|---|
| **a** 14.4 ÷ 4 | **b** 21.0 ÷ 6 | **c** 58.5 ÷ 9 | **d** 62.3 ÷ 7 |
| **e** 59.5 ÷ 5 | **f** 9.28 ÷ 8 | **g** 43.75 ÷ 7 | **h** 40.95 ÷ 9 |

**4** A meal for 8 people costs £74.56. If they share the
bill equally, how much does each person pay?

**5** There are 8 lamp posts from one end of South Lane
to the other. South Lane is 223.3 m long.
How many spaces are there between these lamp posts?
How long is each space?

MyMaths.co.uk

Q 1008    SEARCH

**Example**

Calculate   $\sqrt{2025} + 15$

- - - - - - - - - - - - - - - - - - - - - - - - - - - - - - - - - - -

Use your calculator.

√ ( 2 0 2 5 ) + 1 5 =   **60**

---

**1** Use a calculator to work these out, using the $x^2$ or
  √ button where required. Give your answers to
  2 decimal places where appropriate.

  **a**  $9 + 2.6^2$        **b**  $11 + 4.1^2$

  **c**  $5.8^2 \times 4$       **d**  $1.8^2 - 0.95$

  **e**  $3.4 \times \sqrt{15.21}$     **f**  $\sqrt{18 - 3}$

  **g**  $\sqrt{12 + 16}$

**2** Use your calculator to work these out. Express
  the remainder as a whole number and interpret
  the units carefully.

  **a**  45 mins ÷ 6      **b**  100 cm ÷ 8      **c**  42 people ÷ 4

**3** Convert these measurements of time to the units
  indicated in brackets.

  **a**  309 minutes       (hours and minutes)

  **b**  78 hours           (days and hours)

  **c**  96 seconds        (minutes and seconds)

  **d**  1240 days         (years and days)

**4** Work out the age of these babies in weeks and days.

  **a**  Flora 353 days     **b**  Lily 267 days     **c**  Zac 124 days

---

⊕ **MyMaths**.co.uk

60 students are entered for an examination and 45 of them pass.
Find the proportion who pass, expressing your answer as
**a** a fraction **b** a percentage.

**a** ÷ 15

$$\frac{45}{60} = \frac{3}{4}$$

÷ 15

**b** × 25

$$\frac{3}{4} = \frac{75}{100} = 75\%$$

× 25

**1** Write each of these fractions as hundredths. Then convert each fraction
to **i** a decimal **ii** a percentage.

**a** $\frac{1}{4}$ **b** $\frac{3}{5}$

**c** $\frac{7}{20}$ **d** $\frac{14}{25}$

**2** There are 24 boys in class 7C. On Wednesday, 6 boys are absent.
**a** How many boys were present on Wednesday?
**b** What proportion of boys were present on Wednesday?
Give your answer as **i** a fraction **ii** a percentage.

**3** The table shows the sports option
chosen by a group of 30 students.
**a** What proportion of the students
chose Rounders?
**b** What proportion of the students
chose Tennis?
**c** What proportion of the students did **not** choose swimming?

| Sport | Frequency |
|---|---|
| Tennis | 12 |
| Swimming | 9 |
| Rounders | 3 |
| Athletics | 6 |

**4** Victoria scores 34 out of 50 in a History test and 84 out of
120 in a Geography test. In which test did she do the best?

MyMaths.co.uk

Q 1037 SEARCH

A recipe for 8 rich scones uses 200 g of self-raising flour.
How much flour is needed for 12 rich scones?

$$\times 1.5 \left( \begin{array}{ll} 8 \text{ rich scones} & 200\,g \text{ flour} \\ 12 \text{ rich scones} & 300\,g \text{ flour} \end{array} \right) \times 1.5$$

12 rich scones need 300 g flour.

**1** The table shows the cost of some blocks
of 'Organic Farmhouse Cheddar cheese'.

Are the numbers in this table in direct
proportion? Explain your answer.

| Amount of cheese | Cost (£) |
|---|---|
| 250 g | £2.25 |
| 500 g | £4.50 |
| 1 kg | £9.00 |

**2** A car uses 10 litres of petrol to travel 120 km.
How far can the car travel on

   **a** 20 litres      **b** 30 litres

   **c** 50 litres      **d** 5 litres of petrol?

**3** A telephone call to New Zealand costs 4p per minute.
Find the cost of a call lasting

   **a** 3 minutes      **b** 5 minutes

   **c** 20 minutes      **d** 30 seconds

**4** Use direct proportion to complete this
table for converting between pounds (£)
and euros (€).

| £ | € |
|---|---|
| 1 | |
| 2 | 3 |
| | 9 |
| 10 | |
| | 30 |

A long, thin piece of wood is cut into pieces with lengths in the ratio of $9:13$. If the shorter piece is 36 cm long, what is the length of the longer piece?

36 cm = 9 parts
4 cm = 1 part
The longer part is 13 parts.
The length of the longer piece is 4 cm × 13 = 52 cm.

**1** Give each ratio in its simplest form.

| | | | |
|---|---|---|---|
| **a** $3:6$ | **b** $9:12$ | **c** $6:9$ | **d** $10:12$ |
| **e** $5:25$ | **f** $36:40$ | **g** $25:40$ | **h** $30:48$ |

**2** Write each ratio in its simplest form.

**a** On a supermarket shelf there are 6 bags of plain flour and 9 bags of self-raising flour.
What is the ratio of plain flour to self-raising flour?

**b** Anne weighs 28 kg and Nicola weighs 40 kg.
What is the ratio of Anne's weight to Nicola's weight?

**c** At a party, 24 children asked for tea and 30 asked for lemonade. What was the ratio of tea to lemonade?

**3** In a recipe for rich scones, the ratio of sugar to flour is $1:8$. How much flour is needed to mix with 25 g sugar?

**4** The heights of two sisters, Shani and Candace, are in the ratio $4:5$. If Shani is 120 cm tall, how tall is Candace?

**5** A jug can exactly fill two cups whose capacities are in the ratio $3:5$. If the smaller cup holds 150 ml, what is the capacity of the larger cup?

**6** A farmer has 60 sheep, 12 of them are black and the rest are white. Find the ratio of black sheep to white sheep.

**MyMaths**.co.uk

Q 1038, 1052 SEARCH

In class 7B there are 3 girls for every 4 boys. There are 21 students in class 7B. Work out the number of girls and boys.

| | |
|---|---|
| If there are 3 girls, there are 4 boys. | 3 + 4 = 7 students |
| If there are 6 girls, there are 8 boys. | 6 + 8 = 14 students |
| If there are 9 girls, there are 12 boys. | 9 + 12 = 21 students |
| There are 9 girls and 12 boys. | |

**1** At a tennis club of 50 members, there are 20 women.
    **a** Write the ratio of women to men.
    **b** Write the ratio of men to women.
    **c** Write the proportion of members that are men.

**2** A recipe for flaky pastry uses 150 g margarine for every 250 g of plain flour.
    **a** Write the ratio of flour to margarine.
    **b** Write the proportion of these ingredients that is flour.

**3** In the United Kingdom, $\frac{3}{16}$ of the red squirrels live in England.
    **a** Write the fraction of red squirrels that live elsewhere in the UK.
    **b** Write the ratio of red squirrels in England to red squirrels in the rest of the UK.

**4** In a box of chocolates the ratio of milk chocolates to dark chocolates is 5 : 4. There are 36 chocolates in the box.
Work out the number of milk and dark chocolates.

**5** In a carton of apple and mango juice, 85% is apple juice and the rest is mango juice.
    **a** Write the ratio of mango juice to apple juice.
    **b** In a 1 litre carton, work out the amount of each type of juice.

Megan lives in Hull. She writes the four letters of her home town on cards, shuffles the cards and then picks one at random.

How likely is it that she picks **a** an L **b** an H **c** a U?

- - - - - - - - - - - - - - - - - - - - - - - - - - - - - - - - - - - - - -

**a** 2 out of 4 or $\frac{2}{4}$, which is $\frac{1}{2}$

**b** 1 out of 4 or $\frac{1}{4}$

**c** 1 out of 4 or $\frac{1}{4}$

H or U    L
 ↓        ↓
$\begin{array}{ccccc} 0 & \frac{1}{4} & \frac{1}{2} & \frac{3}{4} & 1 \end{array}$

**1** Copy this probability scale and place these cards at the correct points on the scale.

$\begin{array}{ccc} 0 & 0.5 & 1 \end{array}$

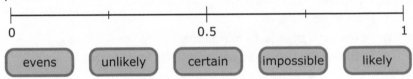

| evens | unlikely | certain | impossible | likely |

**2** Draw a probability scale like the one in question **1**.
Place an arrow and the corresponding letter of each event below at the correct point of your scale.
- **a** If you toss a coin you will get a 'head'.
- **b** If you throw a dice you will get a 'six'.
- **c** Tomorrow will be Saturday.
- **d** You will wear your winter coat tomorrow.
- **e** You will be struck by lightning on the way home tonight.
- **f** Your Maths teacher will turn out to be a member of MI5.

**3** An octagonal spinner is spun.
How likely is it that the score will be

**a** 8          **b** 4 or 5          **c** an odd number?

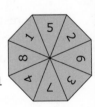

Use this scale to help you.

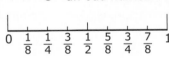

$\begin{array}{ccccccccc} 0 & \frac{1}{8} & \frac{1}{4} & \frac{3}{8} & \frac{1}{2} & \frac{5}{8} & \frac{3}{4} & \frac{7}{8} & 1 \end{array}$

**⊞ MyMaths**.co.uk

Q 1209   SEARCH

Where Jack lives, the probability of a November morning being frosty is 60%.

**a** How would you describe this probability?

**b** On how many November mornings can Jack expect to find the weather frosty?

---

**a** Likely, because it is greater than 'evens', which is 50%.

**b** The number of mornings = 60% of 30 = $\frac{60}{100}$ × 30 = 18

**1** The table shows a football team's chances of winning or losing a match.

| Outcome | Probability |
|---------|-------------|
| win | $\frac{1}{2}$ |
| draw | $\frac{1}{6}$ |
| lose | $\frac{1}{3}$ |

The team has 24 matches to play. How many can they expect to

**a** win          **b** draw          **c** lose?

**2** Explain whether or not the outcomes for these are equally likely.

**a** A footballer taking a penalty may score or miss.

**b** If I am stopped at a level crossing, the train may come from either direction.

**c** If I approach some traffic lights, I may have to stop or I may be able to proceed.

**d** North of the Arctic Circle there may be daylight or darkness.

**e** If a meteorite falls on the Earth, it may fall on either the northern or southern hemisphere.

**f** If a meteorite falls on the Earth, it may fall on either land or sea.

There are 16 bags of sugar on a supermarket shelf.
12 of them contain white sugar and 4 contain brown sugar.
If a bag is taken at random, what is the probability that it
contains **a** white sugar **b** brown sugar?

**a** $\dfrac{12}{16} = \dfrac{3}{4}$  **b** $\dfrac{4}{16} = \dfrac{1}{4}$

**1** The letters of the word PEPPER are written on cards.
The cards are shuffled and one is picked at random.
What is the probability that it shows
  **a** a P  **b** an E?

**2** Penelope writes the letters of her name on cards.
She shuffles them and picks one at random.
What is the probability that it shows
  **a** an E  **b** a P  **c** a vowel  **d** a consonant?

**3** In class 4A there are 18 girls with dark hair, 10 girls with
fair hair and 2 girls with red hair. The teacher picks
one girl at random to give out some books.
What is the probability that she will have
  **a** dark hair  **b** fair hair  **c** red hair?

**4** On a supermarket shelf there are 8 packets of plain crisps,
5 packets of cheese and onion crisps, 3 packets of salt
and vinegar crisps and 4 packets of smoky bacon crisps.
If a packet is removed at random, what is the probability
that it will contain
  **a** plain crisps
  **b** cheese and onion crisps
  **c** salt and vinegar crisps
  **d** smoky bacon crisps
  **e** strawberry crisps?

A football club has 36 players available. Eight of the players are left-footed. What is the probability that a footballer from this club is left-footed?

- - - - - - - - - - - - - - - - - - - - - - - - - - - - - - - - - - - -

Probability of being left-footed $= \dfrac{\text{Number of left-footed players}}{\text{Total number of players}}$

The probability is $\dfrac{8}{36} = \dfrac{2}{9}$

1   A nursery asks each child's parents whether or not the child has had the MMR vaccination. The table shows the results.
Use the results to estimate the probability that the next child will have had the MMR vaccination.

| Yes | No |
|------|-----|
| 43 | 7 |

2   Jason has a bag of red and blue balls. He selects a ball at random, records its colour and replaces the ball in the bag. The table shows his results.
Use the results to estimate the probability that the next ball he draws will be red.

| Red | Blue |
|------|-------|
| 12 | 28 |

3   A spinner is spun 250 times. The table shows the results.

| Colour | Black | White | Grey |
|-----------|--------|--------|-------|
| Frequency | 120 | 70 | 60 |

a   Estimate the probability that the next spin will show
    i   black        ii   white        iii   grey.
    Give your answers as percentages.
b   Which of these pictures is most likely to be this spinner? Explain your answer.

**a** Use a Venn diagram to sort the letters of the word 'FRACTIONS' into:
V = {the set of vowels}   and   W = {the letters in the word 'MATHS'}.
Use numbers to represent the number of letters in each set.
**b** How many letters are in the union of the sets?

- - - - - - - - - - - - - - - - - - - - - - - - - - - - - - - - - - - - -

**a** Vowels: A I O
Letters in 'MATHS': A T S
Letter A is in the intersection.
Remaining letters: F R C N
**b** 2 + 1 + 2 = 5 letters

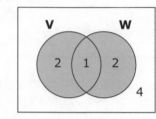

1 A warehouse uses a four-digit code
for each item it stores.
The warehouse manager picks eight codes.
Sort the codes into each Venn diagram.
Use numbers to represent the number of codes in each set.

| X32C | Y23A | X11A | Z23B |
| X12B | Z33A | Y13B | X21C |

**a**
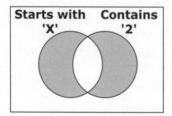

**b**
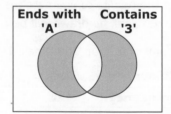

2 Katya asks 20 students at her school if they
are playing hockey or tennis in PE this term.
Her results are shown on the Venn diagram.
How many students are

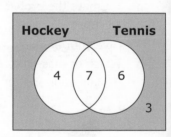

**a** in the intersection of hockey and tennis
**b** playing hockey
**c** not playing tennis
**d** in the union of hockey and tennis?
**e** Describe the shaded region in words.
**f** What fraction of students are playing either hockey or tennis,
but not both?

MyMaths.co.uk

Q 1235   SEARCH

**add, addition (+)**

Addition is the sum of two numbers or quantities.

**adjacent (side)**

Adjacent sides are next to each other and are joined by a common vertex.

**algebra**

Algebra is the branch of mathematics where symbols or letters are used to represent numbers.

**amount**

Amount means total.

**angle: acute, obtuse, right, reflex**

An angle is formed when two straight lines cross or meet each other at a point. The size of an angle is measured by the amount one line has been turned in relation to the other.

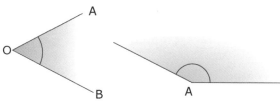

An acute angle is less than 90°

An obtuse angle is more than 90° but less than 180°

A right angle is a quarter of a turn, or 90°

A reflex angle is more than 180° but less than 360°

| | |
|---|---|
| **angles at a point** | Angles at a point add up to 360°. |

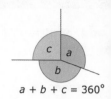

$$a + b + c = 360°$$

| | |
|---|---|
| **angles on a straight line** | Angles on a straight line add up to 180°. |

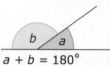

$$a + b = 180°$$

| | |
|---|---|
| **approximate, approximately** | An approximate value is a value that is close to the actual value of a number. |
| **approximately equal to ($\approx$)** | Approximately equal to means almost the same size. |
| **area: square millimetre, square centimetre, square metre, square kilometre** | The area of a surface is a measure of its size. |
| **average** | An average is a representative value of a set of data. |
| **axis, axes** | An axis is one of the lines used to locate a point in a coordinate system. |
| **bar chart** | A bar chart is a diagram that uses rectangles of equal width to display data. The frequency is given by the height of the rectangle. |
| **bar-line graph** | A bar-line graph is a diagram that uses lines to display data. The lengths of the lines are proportional to the frequencies. |

| | |
|---|---|
| **base** | The lower horizontal edge of a shape or solid is usually called the base. Similarly, the base of a solid is its lower face. 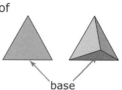 |
| **between** | Between means in the space bounded by two limits. |
| **brackets** | Operations within brackets should be carried out first. |
| **calculate, calculation** | Calculate means work out using a mathematical procedure. |
| **calculator** | You can use a calculator to perform calculations. |
| **cancel, cancellation** | A fraction is cancelled down by dividing the numerator and denominator by a common factor. $$\div 8$$ For example, $\frac{24}{40} = \frac{3}{5}$ $$\div 8$$ |
| **capacity: litre** | Capacity is a measure of the amount of liquid a 3D shape will hold. |
| **centre of rotation** | The centre of rotation is the fixed point about which a rotation takes place.  |
| **certain** | An event that is certain will definitely happen. |
| **chance** | Chance is the probability of something happening. |

**class interval**    A class interval is a group that you put data into to make it easier to handle.

**common factor**    A common factor is a factor of two or more numbers.
For example, 2 is a common factor of 4 and 10.

**compare**    Compare means to assess the similarity of.

**congruent**    Congruent shapes are exactly the same shape and size.

**consecutive**    Consecutive means following on in order.
For example, 2, 3 and 4 are consecutive integers.

**construct**    To construct means to draw a line, angle or shape accurately.

**continue**    Continue means carry on.

**convert**    Convert means to change.

**coordinate pair**    A coordinate pair is a pair of numbers that give the position of a point on a coordinate grid.
For example, (3, 2) means 3 units across and 2 units up from the origin.

**coordinate point**    A coordinate point is the point described by a coordinate pair.

**coordinates**    Coordinates are the numbers that make up a coordinate pair.

**data**    Data are pieces of information.

**data collection sheet**    A data collection sheet is a sheet used to collect data. It is sometimes a list of questions with tick boxes for collecting answers.

| | |
|---|---|
| **decimal number** | A decimal number is a number written using a decimal point. |
| **decimal place (dp)** | Each column after the decimal point is called a decimal place.<br>For example, 0.65 has two decimal places (2 dp). |
| **degree (°)** | A degree is a measure of turn. There are 360° in a full turn. |
| **denominator** | The denominator is the bottom number in a fraction. It shows how many parts there are in total. |
| **difference** | You find the difference between two amounts by subtracting one from the other. |
| **digit** | A digit is any of the numbers 0, 1, 2, 3, 4, 5, 6, 7, 8, 9. |
| **direction** | The direction is the orientation of a line in space. |
| **distance** | The distance between two points is the length of the line that joins them. |
| **divide, division (÷)** | Divide means share equally. |
| **divisible, divisibility** | A whole number is divisible by another if there is no remainder left. |
| **divisor** | The divisor is the number that does the dividing.<br>For example, in 14 ÷ 2 = 7 the divisor is 2. |
| **double, halve** | Double means multiply by two. Halve means divide by two. |

**edge (of solid)**

An edge is a line along which two faces of a solid meet.

edge

**equal (sides, angles)**

Equal sides are the same length. Equal angles are the same size.

**equally likely**

Events are equally likely if they have the same probability.

**equals (=)**

Equals means having exactly the same value or size.

**equation**

An equation is a statement using an = sign to link two expressions.

**equivalent, equivalence**

Equivalent fractions are fractions with the same value.

**estimate**

An estimate is an approximate answer.

**evaluate**

Evaluate means find the value of an expression.

**exact, exactly**

Exact means completely accurate.
For example, 3 divides into 6 exactly.

**experiment**

An experiment is a test or investigation to gather evidence for or against a theory.

**expression**

An expression is a collection of numbers and symbols linked by operations but not including an equals sign.

**face**

A face is a flat surface of a solid.

face

| | |
|---|---|
| **factor** | A factor is a number that divides exactly into another number. <br> For example, 3 and 7 are factors of 21. |
| **fair** | In a fair experiment there is no bias towards any particular outcome. |
| **fraction** | A fraction is a way of describing a part of a whole. $\frac{2}{5}$ |
| **frequency** | Frequency is the number of times something occurs. |
| **frequency diagram** | A frequency diagram uses bars to display grouped data. The height of each bar gives the frequency of the group, and there is no space between the bars. |
| **function** | A function is a rule. <br> For example, +2, –3, ×4 and ÷5 are all functions. |
| **function machine** | A function machine links an input value to an output value by performing a function. |
| **generalise** | Generalise means formulate a general statement or rule. |
| **generate** | Generate means produce. |
| **graph** | A graph is a diagram that shows a relationship between variables. |
| **greater than (>)** | Greater than means more than. <br> For example, 4 > 3. |
| **grid** | A grid is used as a background to plot coordinate points. It is usually squared. |

| | |
|---|---|
| **height** | Height is the vertical distance from the base to the top of a shape. |
| **highest common factor (HCF)** | The highest common factor is the largest factor that is common to two or more numbers.<br>For example, the HCF of 12 and 8 is 4. |
| **horizontal** | Horizontal means flat and level with the ground. |
| **hundredth** | A hundredth is 1 out of 100.<br>For example, 0.05 has 5 hundredths. |
| **impossible** | An event is impossible if it definitely cannot happen. |
| **improper fraction** | An improper fraction is a fraction where the numerator is greater than the denominator.<br>For example, $\frac{8}{5}$ is an improper fraction. |
| **increase, decrease** | Increase means make greater.<br>Decrease means make less. |
| **input, output** | Input is data fed into a machine or process. Output is the data produced by a machine or process. |
| **integer** | An integer is a positive or negative whole number (including zero). The integers are ..., −3, −2, −1, 0, 1, 2, 3, ... |
| **interpret** | You interpret data whenever you make sense of it. |
| **intersect, intersection** | Two lines intersect at the point, or points, where they cross. |

intersection

**interval**

An interval is the size of a class or group in a frequency table.

**inverse**

An inverse operation has the opposite effect to the original operation.

For example, multiplication is the inverse of division.

**label**

A label is a description of a diagram or object.

**length: millimetre, centimetre, metre, kilometre; mile, foot, inch**

Length is a measure of distance. It is often used to describe one dimension of a shape.

**less than (<)**

Less than means smaller than.

For example, 3 is less than 4 or 3 < 4.

**likelihood**

Likelihood is the probability of an event happening.

**likely**

An event is likely if it will happen more often than not.

**line**

A line joins two points.

**line of symmetry**

A line of symmetry is a line about which a 2D shape can be folded so that one half of the shape fits exactly on the other half.

**line symmetry**

A shape has line symmetry if it has a line of symmetry.

**lowest common multiple (LCM)**

The lowest common multiple is the smallest multiple that is common to two or more numbers.

For example, the LCM of 4 and 6 is 12.

**lowest terms**

A fraction is in its lowest terms when the numerator and denominator have no common factors.

| | |
|---|---|
| **mapping** | A mapping is a rule that can be applied to a set of numbers to give another set of numbers. |
| **mass: gram, kilogram; ounce, pound** | Mass is a measure of the amount of matter in an object. An object's mass is closely linked to its weight. |
| **mean** | The mean is an average value found by adding all the data values and dividing by the number of pieces of data. |
| **measure** | When you measure something you find the size of it. |
| **median** | The median is an average which is the middle value when the data is arranged in size order. |
| **mirror line** | A mirror line is a line of symmetry. 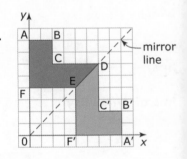 |
| **mixed number** | A mixed number has a whole number part and a fraction part. For example, $3\frac{1}{2}$ is a mixed number. |
| **modal class** | The modal class is the most commonly occurring class when the data is grouped. It is the class with the highest frequency. |
| **mode** | The mode is an average which is the data value that occurs most often. |

**multiple**

A multiple of an integer is the product of that integer and any other.

For example, 6 × 4 = 24 and 6 × 12 = 72 are multiples of 6.

**multiply, multiplication (×)**

Multiplication is the operation of combining two numbers or quantities to form a product.

**nearest**

Nearest means the closest value.

**negative**

A negative number is a number less than zero.

**net**

A net is a 2D arrangement that can be folded to form a solid shape.

***n*th term**

The *n*th term is the general term of a sequence.

**numerator**

The numerator is the top number in a fraction. It shows how many parts you are dealing with.

**object, image**

The object is the original shape before a transformation. An image is the same shape after a transformation.

**operation**

An operation is a rule for processing numbers or objects. The basic operations are addition, subtraction, multiplication and division.

**opposite (sides, angles)**

Opposite means across from.

**order**

To order means to arrange according to size or importance.

**order of operations**

The conventional order of operations is BIDMAS: brackets first, then indices, then division and multiplication, then addition and subtraction.

**order of rotation symmetry**

The order of rotation symmetry is the number of times that a shape will fit onto itself during a full turn.

**origin**

The origin is the point where the $x$- and $y$-axes cross, that is $(0, 0)$.

**outcome**

An outcome is the result of a trial or experiment.

**parallel**

Two lines that always stay the same distance apart are parallel. Parallel lines never cross or meet.

**partition; part**

To partition means to split a number into smaller amounts, or parts.

For example, 57 could be split into 50 + 7, or 40 + 17.

**percentage (%)**

A percentage is a fraction expressed as the number of parts per hundred.

**perimeter**

The perimeter of a shape is the distance around it. It is the total length of the edges.

**perpendicular**

Two lines are perpendicular to each other if they meet at a right angle.

**pie chart**

A pie chart uses a circle to display data. The angle at the centre of a sector is proportional to the frequency.

**place value**

The place value is the value of a digit in a decimal number.

For example, in 3.65 the digit 6 has a value of 6 tenths.

| **polygon: pentagon, hexagon, octagon** | A polygon is a closed shape with three or more straight edges. |
|---|---|

 A pentagon has five sides

 A hexagon has six sides.

 An octagon has eight sides.

| **positive** | A positive number is greater than zero. |
|---|---|
| **predict** | Predict means forecast in advance. |
| **prime** | A prime number is a number that has exactly two different factors, itself and 1. |
| **probability** | Probability is a measure of how likely an event is. |
| **probability scale** | A probability scale is a line numbered 0 to 1 or 0% to 100% on which you place an event based on its probability. |
| **product** | The product is the result of a multiplication. |
| **proportion** | Proportion compares the size of a part to the size of a whole. You can express a proportion as a fraction, decimal or percentage. |
| **protractor (angle measurer)** | A protractor is an instrument for measuring angles in degrees. |
| **quadrant** | A coordinate grid is divided into four quadrants by the $x$- and $y$-axes. |

| quadrilateral: | A quadrilateral is a polygon with four sides. |
| --- | --- |
| arrowhead, kite, parallelogram, rectangle, rhombus, square, trapezium | |

rectangle      parallelogram      kite

  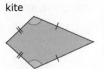

All angles are right angles.    Two pairs of parallel sides.    Two pairs of adjacent sides equal.

rhombus      square      trapezium

  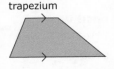

All sides the same length. Opposite angles equal.    All sides and angles equal.    One pair of parallel sides.

**questionnaire**

A questionnaire is a list of questions used to gather information in a survey.

**quotient**

A quotient is the result of a division.

**random**

A selection is random if each object or number is equally likely to be chosen.

**range**

The range is the difference between the largest and smallest values in a set of data.

**ratio**

Ratio compares the size of one part with the size of another part.

**reflect, reflection**

A reflection is a transformation in which corresponding points in the object and the image are the same distance from the mirror line.

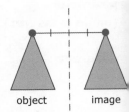

object      image

**reflection symmetry**    A shape has reflection symmetry if it has a line of symmetry.

**regular**    A regular polygon has equal sides and equal angles.

**relationship**    A relationship is a link between objects or numbers.

**remainder**    A remainder is the amount left over when one quantity is exactly divided by another.
For example, 9 ÷ 4 = 2 remainder 1 or 2 r 1.

**represent**    You represent data whenever you display it in the form of a diagram.

**rotate, rotation**    A rotation is a transformation in which every point in the object turns through the same angle relative to a fixed point.

**rotation symmetry**    A shape has rotation symmetry if when turned it fits onto itself more than once during a full turn.

**round**    You round a number by expressing it to a given degree of accuracy.
For example, 639 is 600 to the nearest 100 and 640 to the nearest 10.

To round to one decimal place means to round to the nearest tenth.
For example, 12.47 is 12.5 to 1 dp.

**rule**    A rule describes the link between objects or numbers.
For example, the rule linking 2 and 6 may be +4 or ×3.

| | |
|---|---|
| **ruler** | A ruler is an instrument for measuring lengths. |
| **sequence** | A sequence is a set of numbers or objects that follow a rule. |
| **shape** | A shape is made by a line or lines drawn on a surface, or by putting surfaces together. |
| **side (of 2D shape)** | A side is a line segment joining vertices. |
| **sign** | A sign is a symbol used to denote an operation. |
| **simplest form** | A fraction (or ratio) is in its simplest form when the numerator and denominator (or parts of the ratio) have no common factors. For example, $\frac{3}{5}$ is expressed in its simplest form. |
| **simplify** | To simplify an expression you gather all like terms together into a single term. |
| **sketch** | A sketch shows the general shape of a graph or diagram. |
| **solid (3D) shape: cube, cuboid, prism, pyramid** | A solid is a shape formed in three-dimensional space. |

cube      cuboid      prism      pyramid

six square faces    six rectangular faces    the end faces are constant    the faces meet at a common vertex

| | |
|---|---|
| **solution (of an equation)** | The solution of an equation is the value of the variable that makes the equation true. |

**solve (an equation)**

To solve an equation you need to find the value of the variable that will make the equation true.

**spin, spinner**

A spinner is an instrument for creating random outcomes, usually in probability experiments.

**square-based pyramid, tetrahedron**

tetrahedron

all faces are equilateral triangles

square-based pyramid

the base is a square

**square number, squared**

If you multiply a number by itself the result is a square number.

For example, 25 is a square number because $5^2 = 5 \times 5 = 25$.

**square root**

A square root is a number that when multiplied by itself is equal to a given number.

For example, $\sqrt{25} = 5$, because $5 \times 5 = 25$.

**statistic, statistics**

Statistics is the collection, display and analysis of information.

**straight-line graph**

When coordinate points lie in a straight line they form a straight-line graph. It is the graph of a linear equation.

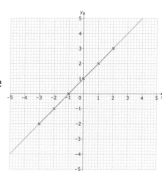

**substitute**

When you substitute you replace part of an expression with its value.

**subtract, subtraction (−)**

Subtraction is the operation that finds the difference in size between two numbers.

**sum**

The sum is the total and is the result of an addition.

**surface, surface area**

The surface area of a solid is the total area of its faces.

**survey**

A survey is an investigation to find information.

**symbol**

A symbol is a letter, number or other mark that represents a number or an operation.

**symmetrical**

A shape is symmetrical if it is unchanged after a rotation or reflection.

**table**

A table is an arrangement of information, numbers or letters, usually in rows and columns.

**tally**

You use a tally mark to represent an object when you collect data. Tally marks are usually made in groups of five to make it easier to count them.

**temperature: degrees Celsius, degrees Fahrenheit**

Temperature is a measure of how hot something is.

**tenth**

A tenth is 1 out of 10 or $\frac{1}{10}$.
For example, 0.5 has 5 tenths.

**term**

A term is a number or object in a sequence. It is also part of an expression.

| | |
|---|---|
| **thousandth** | A thousandth is 1 out of 1000 or $\frac{1}{1000}$.<br>For example, 0.002 has 2 thousandths. |
| **three-dimensional (3D)** | Any solid shape is three-dimensional. |
| **total** | The total is the result of an addition. |
| **transformation** | A transformation moves a shape from one place to another. |
| **translate, translation** | A translation is a transformation in which every point in an object moves the same distance and direction.<br>It is a sliding movement. |

**triangle: equilateral, isosceles, scalene, right-angled**

A triangle is a polygon with three sides.

equilateral

three equal sides

isosceles

two equal sides

scalene

no equal sides

right-angled

one angle is 90°

| | |
|---|---|
| **two-dimensional (2D)** | A flat shape has two dimensions: length and width or base and height. |
| **unknown** | An unknown is a variable. You can often find its value by solving an equation. |
| **value** | The value is the amount an expression or variable is worth. |

**variable**                              A variable is a symbol that can take
                                          any value.

**vertex, vertices**                      A vertex of a shape is a point at which two
                                          or more edges meet. The plural of vertex is
                                          vertices.

                                          vertex

**vertical**                              Vertical means straight up and down.

**vertically opposite angles**            When two straight lines
                                          cross they form two pairs
                                          of equal angles called
                                          vertically opposite angles.

                                          $a = c$   $b = d$

**whole**                                 The whole is the full amount.

**width**                                 Width is a dimension of an object describing
                                          how wide it is.

**_x_-axis, _y_-axis**                    On a coordinate grid, the _x_-axis is the horizontal
                                          axis and the _y_-axis is the vertical axis.

**x-coordinate,**
**y-coordinate**

The *x*-coordinate is the distance along the *x*-axis. The *y*-coordinate is the distance along the *y*-axis.

For example, (−2, −3) is -2 along the x-axis and -3 along the y-axis.

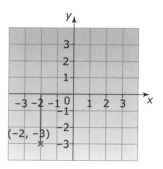

**zero**

Zero is nought or nothing. A zero place holder is used to show the place value of other digits in a number.